NICHOLAS WOOLLEY [...] versity and intended after [...] the Church of England. U[...] [...] what he saw as the contradictions within Christianity, he decided that preaching to others would be impossible. His career has been varied. After National Service as a pilot in the Fleet Air Arm, he went to Turkey, where he taught English. He worked in the theatre, ran a small company that published greetings cards and then became an administrator at the London School of Economics. He joined *The Times Educational Supplement* as a journalist, eventually transferring to *The Times*'s foreign desk. The BBC recruited him in the mid-Sixties for their expanding current affairs programmes on radio. For several years he was a reporter and presenter on *The World at One*, *The World this Weekend* and *PM*. In the mid-Seventies he moved to television current affairs, working on such programmes as *Nationwide*, *Panorama* and *Newsnight*, as well as making documentaries, one of which was the inspiration for this book. When he is not writing he works as a free-lance television reporter and presenter for ITN, Channel 4 and the BBC.

SUE CLAYTON spent the first twenty years of her life within two miles of the north Norfolk village of Terrington St John. After leaving school she joined Barclays Bank and before long was travelling around East Anglia as a relief cashier. She then worked at the company's head office in London, where her future husband, Tim, was studying jewellery design. After qualifying, he set up a workshop in King's Lynn, and he and Sue were married. Over the next five years they had four children, expanded their business into antique-dealing, moved shop and completely renovated the house they had bought in the village in which Sue had grown up.

JUST FOR WILLIAM

A Family's Fight against Leukaemia

♦

NICHOLAS WOOLLEY
with
SUE CLAYTON

PENGUIN BOOKS

PENGUIN BOOKS

Published by the Penguin Group
27 Wrights Lane, London w8 5tz, England
Viking Penguin Inc., 40 West 23rd Street, New York, New York 10010, USA
Penguin Books Australia Ltd, Ringwood, Victoria, Australia
Penguin Books Canada Ltd, 2801 John Street, Markham, Ontario, Canada l3r 1b4
Penguin Books (NZ) Ltd, 182–190 Wairau Road, Auckland 10, New Zealand

Penguin Books Ltd, Registered Offices: Harmondsworth, Middlesex, England

First published 1989
1 3 5 7 9 10 8 6 4 2

Made and printed in Great Britain by
Richard Clay Ltd, Bungay, Suffolk
Filmset in Monophoto 9 on 11pt Ehrhardt

CONTENTS

◆

People in this Story   vii

Maps   viii–ix

Part One   1

Part Two   101

Postscript by Dr M. K. Brenner   189

PEOPLE IN THIS STORY

◆

William Clayton, aged nine
Tim and Sue Clayton, William's parents
Naomi and Harriet, William's younger sisters
Edward, William's younger brother

Robert and Dorothy Clayton, William's paternal grandparents
Neville and Jean Poole, William's maternal grandparents

Michael and Erica Clayton, Tim's brother and sister-in-law
Ann and Michael Horner, Tim's sister and brother-in-law
David Clayton, Tim's brother; and Jo, David's fiancée

The Rev. Robert Wright, vicar
Kathleen Appleby, village school teacher
Rosemary Wood, a friend of Sue Clayton
Claire Shewring, Tim Clayton's assistant
Ken Doran, family doctor

Jane Tizard, paediatric registrar, Addenbrooke's Hospital

Malcolm Brenner, senior lecturer and consultant, Royal Free Hospital
Paul Roderick, senior house officer, Royal Free Hospital
Robert Simons, consultant anaesthetist, Royal Free Hospital
Teresa Tate, consultant radiotherapist, Royal Free Hospital
David Lee, charge nurse, Royal Free Hospital
Dorothy Jordan, sister, Royal Free Hospital
Robert Milnes, head teacher, Royal Free Hospital
Jane Horne, teacher, Royal Free Hospital

Eduardo and Fernanda Cunha, parents of little Eduardo, visitors from
    Portugal
Vasil and Patra Kitsa, parents of Angeliki and Helen, visitors from
    Greece

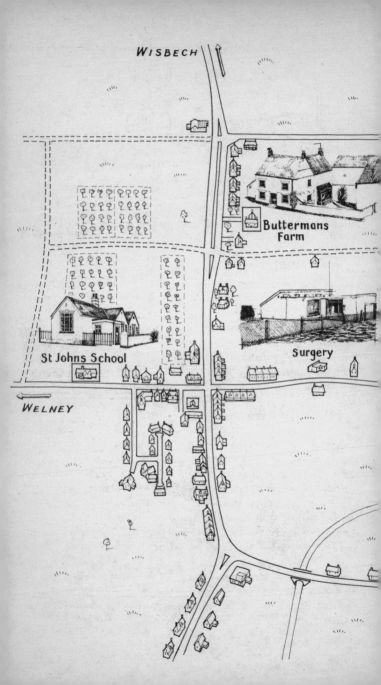

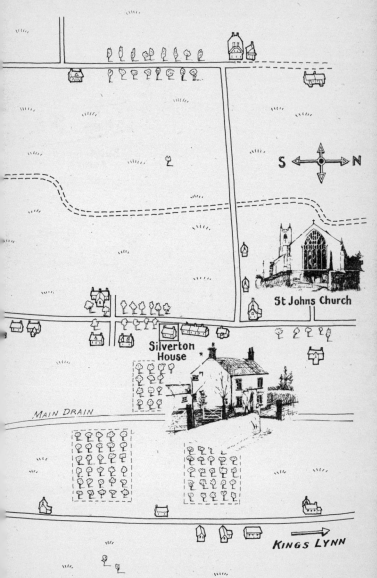

S ←→ N

St Johns Church

Silverton House

MAIN DRAIN

KINGS LYNN

◆ *PART ONE* ◆

CHAPTER 1

'Is Grandpa dead yet?' asked William.

Coming from a nine-year-old, across the breakfast-table, the question might have sounded unfeeling, even impertinent. To William's father, back from a night spent beside his own father's sickbed, it did not seem so. Indeed, it was more and more frequently asked by all the family.

To William, Grandpa Clayton seemed a very old man. For more than a year he had been resisting the encroachment of Hodgkin's disease, a cancer of the blood allied to leukaemia. At Christmas, only a month ago, he seemed to be approaching a peaceful end. Then he rallied. The painful days, dragging on through January, seemed a useless extension of life. As William's father, Tim, said later: 'Pa couldn't understand why he hadn't died. He was ready to die; he wanted to die. I think towards the end he felt cheated that he'd suffered as much as he did.'

William was a serious-minded and straightforward boy. His round face and round glasses sometimes gave him a studious air. He knew his grandfather well. When, after school one day in the middle of February, Tim told the four children that their grandfather had died, William commented: 'Well, he's got what he wanted. He wanted to go to heaven.'

'Is he in the bed, then, Mummy, or is he in heaven?' At six, Harriet Clayton had a practical turn of mind.

'Well, his body's in the bed, but he's really in heaven.'

'When can we join him? Can I go now?'

Neither Tim nor his wife, Sue, thought the moment appropriate for metaphysical debate. 'No. Not now. We've got to go home.'

But William was right: his grandfather, Robert, had believed in heaven with unusual conviction. Indeed, he was an unusual man, whose influence on the family would be felt in unexpected ways.

Robert Clayton was brought up to farm the family land at Welney, amid the flat horizons and open skies of the fens on the Cambridgeshire–Norfolk border. He lived comfortably. His foursquare, yellow-brick house, a little apart from the village, looked south across the fen to the spire of Ely cathedral ten miles away.

He was a good farmer, but not, by his wife's account, a good man. According to family tradition, he was 'rather lively in his youth, a bit of a lad, with a strong liking for drink'. Then, during the Second World War, his style of life suddenly changed. He underwent that comparatively rare experience: immediate, indeed almost instantaneous, religious conversion. He became a gospel preacher. He belonged to no denomination, but he became a familiar figure in tin tabernacles and little chapels all over East Anglia. In the summer, he would set up his tent in small towns and villages and preach to anyone who would listen.

But for Tim Clayton and Robert's three other children, life was not devoted entirely to religion. When Tim was William's age, at the end of the 1950s, they found their amusements in the water-meadows and old orchards of the neighbourhood. They were often amusements that, in later life, Tim would not have approved for William. Tim was not above stealing a few of his mother's hens' eggs and putting them on one side until they were rotten enough to be used in gang fights; or slipping out at night from his bedroom window to shoot pigeons as they sat on their nests, dazzled by the light of a torch. It was a useful way of earning a few extra shillings from an aged aunt.

Faith was not obligatory. As Tim recalls: 'Pa didn't believe in "offering his children to the Lord" when they were babies. You weren't baptized until you asked to be baptized, and you were old enough to understand.

'I have a very simple belief that was taught me by my father – for which I can do nothing but thank and admire him – which I've tried to pass on to William and the other children. But when I was a teenager, my father did embarrass me terribly by the way he tackled people he wanted to save. You couldn't spend five minutes in his company without becoming aware of his beliefs. If I objected, his answer was simple – "If you saw a blind man walking towards a precipice, wouldn't you say 'Stop'?" But I felt that not everybody is totally blind; and not everybody is right on the edge of the precipice. They didn't need to be buttonholed and embarrassed or frightened into listening.'

Tim's wife, Sue, remembers the first time she met his father.

'I'd only been going out with Tim a fortnight or three weeks. He came in a van with messages plastered all over it – you couldn't avoid

4

seeing it coming. Tim called it a travelling textmobile. And you're on the bus-station, you're sixteen, seventeen, with your boyfriend. This van draws up on the other side of the bus-station. "Hulloa, boy. Over here, boy. Over here." And you think, "Crumbs, is he talking to us?" "Oh . . . that's my father." And you're introduced to this great big man, totally bald, who you think must be some eccentric. And he's dressed up in a dark suit, with a starched white collar and white driving-gloves. And he was so loud. I felt that the whole bus-station knew of his presence.

'The next time I met him, we were at Dereham. And that was an even bigger eye-opener, because he had the tent up. He was holding a series of children's meetings. I couldn't believe that he and Gran were living in this van, with the tent next to it.

'I got used to him in the end, and so did William and the younger three as they grew up. They used to see the van going round the country. William enjoyed going with Pa to the old people's home and helping him with the service. He would find the hymns for the old ladies. Grandpa used to babysit; and he'd come to the school prize-giving and the Nativity play. When he was with the children, he used to relate whatever they were doing to the Bible. If Naomi and Harriet were fighting, he'd talk about Naomi in the Book of Ruth; and when we had meals at home, he'd say grace – but he wouldn't just give ordinary thanks. He'd make up his own prayer, and sometimes it seemed to go on for ever. But the children were used to it. They got on with him very well.

'Before Tim and I got married, my father warned me: Tim was all right, but his father . . .! But then, my father has no religious beliefs whatsoever. It was a pity, really. They had a lot in common. They were both farmers. They both knew everybody, everything that was going on. They were both fond of the children. But when they got on to religion, my father used to mutter to himself, "Silly old fool!" And then he'd try and end it by turning to Mum and saying, "Isn't it time for a cup of tea, Mother?"'

CHAPTER 2

On 13 March, a month after his grandfather's funeral, William went swimming with a school group, to raise money to buy a computer. William was a keen and energetic swimmer, thrashing through the water, his white-blond hair plastered over his begoggled face. On this occasion, however, he felt he had disappointed his sponsors: 'I didn't do as many lengths as I really ought to have been able to do. A girl of my age did forty lengths in half an hour, and I only did about thirty-six.'

No one thought much about it. Usually, William's mother watched him swim. This time she couldn't. She had to be with her youngest child, Edward, who had spent the day in hospital having an operation to repair a hernia. He was not quite five then, but he remembers the day well. 'They had to cut me and take the lump out – they put you to sleep, and then it didn't hurt. If you were awake and they did it, then it would hurt badly. So they sent me to sleep. That was horrible, but when I was asleep, it was all right. They got a gas lead and put it in my mouth. They said "Open wide", and then they put it in and switched it on, and then it starts to make you cry. When you've finished crying, then you go to sleep. Afterwards, I had to walk very, very slowly.'

It was the latest episode in what seemed to be a run of bad luck. In the last few months all the children had fallen victims to an outbreak of mumps. Robert's illness had affected the whole family, and his death, however welcome a relief from pain, could only cause Tim grief. At the same time Sue had been worried about one of her sisters, who had been suffering a prolonged nervous breakdown. Everybody was in need of a respite.

From childhood Tim and Sue had always lived within a few miles of each other, and their relations mostly still did. Tim's eldest brother, Michael, farmed the family land at Welney; his sister, Ann, lived in the family house; only David had moved away, to Hertfordshire.

Sue's parents lived at Butterman's Farm, within walking distance. Like Tim's father, Sue's father, Neville Poole, was a farmer, though he was some twenty years younger than Grandpa Clayton had been.

'I know I'm his daughter,' Sue says, 'but I like to think he's one of the best farmers in the district. He farms a little over a hundred acres, but it's his own land. He's better off, really, than bigger farmers who have borrowed up to the hilt and are running into trouble with the bank. He's what you might call old-fashioned: he thinks you've got to put as much into the land as you take out. And he looks the part. He always wears braces – he says he wouldn't give them up for ten pounds a week.'

When Sue left school, she joined a local bank. She began studying for her banker's examinations, until she realized that, in those days, promotion for a woman beyond a certain point was so unlikely as not to be worth considering. Her father gave her a car, and the bank employed her to fill temporary vacancies in branches all over northern East Anglia. Later she did the same thing in London, living in a hotel during the week and coming home at weekends.

Tim had begun courting Sue when she was still at school. Tim's own education at his local secondary modern school had produced little but an interest in art and metalwork.

'My first job when I left school was shepherding on the washes at home at Welney, working for a chap in the village. At one stage we had the best part of a thousand sheep, half of which had got lung-worm and the other half liver-fluke. So you had to keep them separate, and probably inject them every other day. It was hard work . . . a pound a day. So having done that all summer, and having got a place at the tech in King's Lynn, it seemed prudent to try for A-levels – and nothing like as gruelling as shepherding.

'I really wanted to be an artist and paint . . . create pictures of some sort. Ever since I can remember, I've always drawn – always. Naturally I specialized in the arts side of things for A-levels, and then went to Cambridge, to the art school. It soon became clear that the type of pictures I was interested in creating wouldn't earn me a living . . . abstract designs, experimental etching, discovering how colours affect one another. Earning a living selling that sort of picture is a very difficult thing to do continuously. You've got to be in a position where – well, you may not be Hockney quality, but you know the right people and you're in the swim of things; and I knew I wasn't.

'I came to jewellery design purely by accident. I did it in an evening class, and the first thing I made was so awful I had to go back, because I knew I could do better than that. At school I hadn't realized that it was possible to earn a living by doing interesting metalwork. But once I started making things that were wearable, I would give them to Sue.

7

She would wear them at work in the bank; a customer would come in and say, "I like that: where did you get it?" Result: instant commission; and instant realization that you could turn a few shillings' worth of silver into an article that would sell for several pounds, purely by your own effort.'

It was some years before Tim and Sue were married. Tim was twenty-five, Sue two years younger. They set up home in a flat a few miles outside King's Lynn. Tim had already embarked on his career as a jewellery designer, with a workshop in the town. Sue went on working until shortly before their first child, William, was born in the summer of 1976. Within a couple of years Tim began to prosper sufficiently to open a jewellery shop in King's Lynn, with workrooms behind it. To use the space economically, he also began dealing in antiques and pictures.

'I do whatever I think will earn me a shilling. If I saw a lawn-mower in a drive-way with a "For Sale" sign and a price which looked like less than I thought it would fetch at the local auction, I'd stop, buy it and drop it off at the auction-rooms . . . and hopefully I'd earn on it. I've always had an interest in buying and selling. The most embarrassing thing was selling Mother's bicycle when I was eight. I didn't quite realize that it's not really the right thing to sell your mother's bicycle without her permission. When the bike disappeared and no one could find it, Father's response was: "Well, I suppose we'd better tell the police it's been stolen." So I panicked, and bought the bike back for more than twice what I'd sold it for.'

As the family grew, Tim and Sue moved to the other side of King's Lynn, down the road towards Wisbech, to the village where Sue had been brought up. Terrington St John is not a village that can be captured on a picture postcard. It lies on the A47 trunk road which links King's Lynn and Norwich to the east with Peterborough and the Midlands to the west. Its geographical centre is the crossroads on the main road, a dangerous junction over which cars, beet-lorries and container-trucks roar in an almost continuous stream. On the crossroads is the village shop, responding to supermarket competition by opening seven days a week. Diagonally opposite, set back behind a gravelled forecourt, plants in tubs, old brickwork newly pointed and a renovated tile-roof proclaim a smart new restaurant. Nearby, a pub; and along the four arms of the crossroads, a straggle of houses, cottages and small businesses. A quarter of a mile down the by-road to the south, beyond the last of the houses, stands the village primary school. It was built

8

about a century ago according to the pattern of the time: red brick surmounted by a gabled slate roof; to one side, an asphalt playground behind iron railings; to the other, the former headmaster's house, its garden now used by the children for lunchtime picnics; behind, a jumble of toilets, outbuildings and Portakabin classrooms. Over the back wall, when the wind is wrong, the smell of pigs floats across the yard. On the other side of the road is the school's sports field, the orchard next to it recently grubbed out.

Northwards, half a mile along the opposite arm of the village crossroads, stands St John's church, with its pinnacled tower and lofty roof. Built of brick and stone, the chancel, nave and porch are clearly separate structures. They testify to the continuing wealth of East Anglia, which allowed the church to be modified and extended over the centuries. All around spread flat fields, marked out by ditches and hedgerows, with a sprinkling of full-grown trees. It is a peaceful scene, although too often the natural sense of the landscape is disrupted by the arbitary punctuation of pylons and power-lines.

The vicar, Robert Wright, has been at Terrington St John for more than a dozen years. 'The population is about eight hundred,' he says. 'It's mainly a commuter village now. Most people work in King's Lynn or Wisbech. In years gone by most of them would have worked in the village, in agriculture or horticulture. There's still agriculture and market-gardening, but the number of people employed is minimal, so most people have to look elsewhere. It's affected the village in the sense that more people have also moved in from outside, particularly since they built the new estate. That's fifty or sixty houses, mainly starter homes . . . couples just starting families – I do quite a lot of baptisms. But the longer one knows the people coming in, the more one realizes that they're related to almost everyone else who's been here a long time.'

Not far from the church, in the last row of houses and bungalows before the village peters out, Tim and Sue found their new home. Silverton House is not as grand as the name, inset into the white-painted brickwork, might suggest. When it was built around the turn of the century, it had only one storey. At some later stage it was improved and the upper floor added, but not, in Tim's view, to a very high standard of workmanship. Set in a square plot of land about a third of an acre in extent, it stands a few yards back from the road. On the ground floor are four rooms, all interconnecting. Inside the kitchen door, a cupboard staircase leads to the first floor, where there is just room for four bedrooms. None of the rooms is very large, and when Tim first took Sue to look at the house it was in such bad condition that she dismissed the idea of living there. But he persuaded her that they could make something of it. Beams were exposed, fireplaces opened up, the kitchen appliances were fitted in pine. Tim was given some old oak bookcases from a church and used them to panel the dining-room. In time, a double garage was built, approached by a small gravel sweep. Usually, a second-hand Volvo estate car and a small van for Tim's business are parked on the gravel.

Over the years, the furnishings in the house were supplemented or replaced by antiques and old pictures, any one of which was liable to be sold if need arose. Tim rarely felt as if they had much money.

'I don't worry about money as such. I worry about paying the bills, which involves having the money. But I don't want to be rich. It took me a long time to learn what money is. Money is purely and simply a tool. You can't dig a garden without a spade, and you can't run a business without money, because it is a necessary commodity.

'There are very few possessions of value that I'd really want to keep. The things I would like to keep most are the least valuable in monetary terms. For example, take that picture, the graveyard scene, with the church wall on the left and the house on the right. There's something very curious about that picture. If you look at the shadow going across the middle of it and over the roof of the house, you realize that the church, which you can't see, must have a spire. And that to me is far more interesting than the fact that it might be worth some money because it's by J. M. Thomas. I'd love to ask the man why he painted the shadow of the church steeple and not the steeple itself. The picture works as a picture because the church wall carries your eye into it, but once you realize the church has got a spire, you'll never, ever look at it again without thinking: Oh, the church with the spire. And you can't even see the church. That's worth far more than a painting I might give hundreds for.'

Against this background, Tim and Sue's four children were growing up. William, the eldest, was approaching his last year in primary school, and his parents were beginning to wonder if he could get a place in the local grammar school. His early school reports refer to him as 'a nice little boy, well-behaved, able and hard-working, even if he does do everything to a loud verbal accompaniment'. If he 'sometimes tends to become muddled over quite simple things and has to have them explained several times', on the other hand he 'never gives up till he has solved the problem'. Later, one teacher noted that 'William wishes to be associated with the older boys, and is often unkindly rejected', but the headmaster put him down as 'a boy of strong character – which sometimes causes clashes, usually short, with other strong-minded individuals'. In any case, William enjoyed school and looked certain to do well.

Naomi, two years younger than William, was described as 'a very bright little girl, with a high reading ability and a very good understanding of number; but she is easily distracted and doesn't always work as hard as she could' . . . 'Naomi is erratic and has defiant days when her work is untidy and very poor indeed. It is very hard to persuade her to produce any!' A clue is provided, perhaps, by the comment that 'Naomi gets bored so quickly. She is capable of so much and produces so little.' More recently, to her parents' relief, Naomi had been 'well-behaved and much more co-operative'.

At six, Harriet appeared to be cast in the same mould as William, 'a well-behaved girl who works hard'. Edward, eighteen months' younger, had only just started school. His parents had been told what they knew already, that Edward was confident, noisy, and 'would stand no nonsense from anybody'.

The first ten years of Tim and Sue's marriage had been devoted to establishing their business, renovating the house and garden and looking after the children. Now, with financial stability in prospect and the children safely at school, they felt there was more to look forward to. They were ready to devote more attention to their own lives. They wanted to spend more time together. They had plans for expanding the business, perhaps finding a better site for the shop; and they had long been considering extending the house or even moving altogether.

In little ways, the family's interests were already widening. Edward got his bicycle. The three older children began to have piano lessons and to practise on the tinny upright in the study. Naomi and Harriet went to dancing-class. William learnt to ride. With the shock of Robert Clayton's death beginning to fade, they were all looking forward to the spring.

One Saturday towards the end of March, a week or so after the school's sponsored swim, William took part in another fund-raising event. This time it was a swimming gala. As he explained, 'It was for leukaemia research. You get five teams from the area, club teams, Gladiators, King's Lynn, Cromer, Dereham, Yarmouth, places like that; and you get points for what you do. I went in for the front crawl, back crawl and the relay. I swam OK, but I was a few seconds slower than normal.'

One of the organizers was Kathleen Appleby, a teacher in the village school. She had a short, trim figure and pale, decisive features, her dark hair always taken back. 'It was a county gala in Norwich, starting at a quarter to seven. William slept all the way there in the coach. Sue said she'd given him a travel-sickness pill. He did his swimming before the interval, and afterwards Rebecca (my daughter) said he walked straight past her as if he was in a dream. Then he slept all the way back on the coach again, but I didn't mention it to anybody.'

Next day was Palm Sunday. Sue's mother, Jean Poole, was a regular churchgoer, unlike her husband. On that day she took the grand-children to church with her, as she often used to do. William was reluctant, and had to be persuaded. Tim commented sharply that if he was well enough to go swimming, he was well enough to go to church.

With the other members of the congregation, William collected his palm from the vicar. The vicar recalled that day, in the light of later events. 'I remember thinking, as he took his palm cross: That's not like William. He just took it and sauntered away – so lifeless.'

At home, William didn't eat much lunch, but at tea with his grand-parents he seemed better. Sue was not worried. William was very fit, and he had never been ill. Some of the bruises he always carried, from his sporting activities or knocks in the playground, were rather red, but she thought nothing of it. It was true that over the last week or two William had been spending less time in his swimming classes: he said he was tired. But both Sue and Tim put that down to doing too much and staying up too late.

Next morning, Sue was paying little attention to William in the bustle of getting all four children ready for school, although he was listless, and took a long time to finish his food. Just before they left, William asked his mother for a drink.

Sue found that unusual. 'William has a drink at breakfast, just one drink; but he said, "I'm thirsty. Can I have another drink?" A little later, I sent him upstairs to clean his teeth. For some reason I was following him, and he said, "Do you know what? When I go upstairs, I sometimes have a job to breathe." And then I was really beginning to think: there's something not quite right. On the other hand, I wondered if William was becoming a hypochondriac. Was he copying his friend Thomas, who had asthma? A few days before, William complained that his legs ached, and then went on a cross-country run.

'So we went to school, and I went in to thank Mrs Appleby for looking after him on Saturday evening at the gala. She said, "Oh, he was fine. He slept all the way there and all the way back"; and then of course I knew there was something wrong – a nine-year-old doesn't sleep in a bus-load of boys.'

An appointment was made for William to go to the local surgery. It was not far, a hundred yards from the village crossroads. William was surprised to be collected again from school. 'What have I got to go to the doctor's for?' he asked.

The family doctor, Ken Doran, had practised at Terrington St John since before Sue and Tim were married. Indeed, before they moved to the village, when Sue was expecting William, she had attended his ante-natal clinic. William and Harriet were contemporaries of two of Ken Doran's children. He knew the family well. 'Sue is not what I would call a frequent attender at the surgery, by any means. A mother with four children you expect to see at least every quarter and usually once a month with one or other of the children. And that makes a difference to your response. It shouldn't, but it does.'

Sue remembers the visit well. 'Ken asked "What's your problem?" I replied, "William's off-colour and he's very pale." "That's part of his make-up," he said. And I went on, "But he's off his food; he doesn't eat very well; he's tired and listless." "Perhaps he needs a tonic." And I would have accepted that. I wasn't all that convinced there was anything wrong with him. But then Ken said, "Well, you're obviously worried about him, to bring him here; so we'll have a look at him." He told William to get on the couch.'

For Dr Doran, the one golden rule is: examine. 'If you don't put your finger on it, you'll put your foot in it. I started at the top, and I felt a few glands, but you feel a few glands often if someone is off-colour. Then I put a hand on his tummy, and bingo! There it was – a big spleen.'

William got dressed and Sue told him to go to the waiting-room. 'I couldn't get him out of the surgery quick enough because I wanted to ask Ken, "Is it what I think it is?" And he said, "What are you thinking of?" I replied "Leukaemia." And I think his words were, "It could be a hundred different things."'

Ken Doran's reaction was that everyday things are the most common: this was very unlikely to be leukaemia. 'I was thinking along the lines of some kind of blood disorder. And I went out of my way to give Sue reasons why he hadn't got leukaemia – you can have an enlarged spleen with glandular fever. I reckon I've seen umpteen lung cancers, several cancers of the gut, two on their last legs. The average GP is picking up a fresh malignancy every two months. You might run for six weeks and not see one, then all of a sudden it's three or four. But I would probably see only one childhood leukaemia in my whole lifetime, perhaps two.'

Statistically, one child in three thousand gets leukaemia. But however long the odds against such a diagnosis, Ken Doran took a sample of William's blood. He sent it for analysis to the local laboratory, if only to reassure Sue. The effect on her was quite different.

'If he'd given me a bottle of tonic for William – and I'm not a tonic person anyway – I would have thought: That's exactly what he needs; it's growing-pains. I would have believed him. I didn't come into the surgery expecting leukaemia at all. I needed reassurance that nothing was wrong. I didn't need a blood test, but the very fact that he suggested that . . . then I just knew. He was trying to say leukaemia was the worst thing, but the least possible thing . . . and he'd let me know the results in a couple of days. But I went out of the surgery convinced that William had leukaemia . . . I *knew*. No one had convinced me: I just knew he had leukaemia.

'I met William in the waiting-room, got in the car and took him straight back to school, because to be quite honest I didn't know what else to do with him. I didn't want to get rid of him, but I just wanted to be on my own. I didn't want to worry him or anything, so I took him back to school and said goodbye as though there was nothing wrong at all. I remember the school fence had blown down across the road, it was so windy.

'But I had to see someone, or talk to someone, so after William went into his classroom I went round to Mrs Appleby's class.'

Mrs Appleby was having her coffee break. 'Sue came in through the outside door and she looked absolutely ashen. I asked, "How did you get on?" and she tried to answer and her voice just broke. I said, "Whatever's the matter?" And she came in and I sat her down in a chair; and she said, "William's very ill. He's got an enlarged spleen." "Well," I said, "that doesn't mean anything." She said, "I think he's got leukaemia." And then she started crying and I started crying. And I went in and told the headmaster to keep the children out for five minutes because Sue was upset.'

Sue was given a cup of coffee. She remembers: 'They soon made me laugh. I didn't just sit there . . . I suppose I felt at least I'd told someone. So I had my coffee, and of course playtime was soon over – it was ten minutes at the most – and I made up my mind I was going to King's Lynn to tell Tim. I can't remember the journey at all, which is quite frightening.'

King's Lynn is a long-established market town, which has kept up with modern fashion by opening its central streets to chain-stores and closing them to traffic. It has a large market square surrounded by elegant buildings, and keeps the comfortable, gentlemanly air it acquired at the height of its prosperity in the eighteenth century when the river port was more important commercially than it is now. Today the wealth of King's Lynn depends on light industry, chemical plants and food processors as much as farming. The local population making Mars bars and Campbell's soups in the factories on the outskirts of the town has been enlarged over the past thirty years by an influx of rehoused Londoners. Natives and newcomers alike complain of the rush-hour traffic-jams.

A few minutes' walk from the centre of King's Lynn, opposite the dilapidated seventeenth-century splendour of St Margaret's church, stands the shop where Tim and Sue sold jewellery and antiques. It was an old building, its single window filled with small pieces of porcelain, silver, glass and jewellery. Inside, pictures lined the walls, and a number of clocks stood on shelves and in display cabinets. Down the centre of the shop, showcases held more silver and curios.

Tim's assistant, Claire, was in the office-cum-junk-room at the back. 'The door opened and I got up to see who it was. It was Sue. I noticed two things: her face was wet, and she was blowing her nose. "Hullo, Sue. Got a cold?" She said, "No, is Tim here?" I told her he was in the workshop. Just then he appeared through the side door. So we were all three in this very tiny space, and I sat down again and got on with my book-work. Sue said to Tim that she'd taken William to the doctor, and the doctor had said that William's spleen was enlarged. It dawned on me that something was very much amiss. I couldn't really get out to leave them on their own . . . there was nowhere to go. So they just stood there talking. I got on with my accounts. Then I said to Sue, "Would you like some coffee?", and she said "Yes." So I fetched a chair and she sat down and had some coffee. Everything happened in slow motion . . . it was very, very odd. Tim stood by the door, Sue sat by the door and I sat in my seat. Sue kept saying, "As soon as he said the spleen was enlarged, I knew what it was."'

Tim Clayton was not convinced. 'Quite honestly, I didn't believe there could possibly be anything wrong, other than some general childhood ailment. I could see that Sue was convinced William had leukaemia, and I said, "Until you've got the blood test, you can't assume that. You've got to assume the best, not the worst."'

The result of the blood test was not expected until Wednesday. For Sue, normal life had to be resumed.

'We didn't want to go home, and there were jobs to be done. I took an iron to be mended. I noticed there were tiles all over the streets, it was such a gale. And I had a hair appointment that afternoon. I kept it . . . there was nothing else to do. I'm very friendly with the hairdresser, and I actually told her. Tim picked me up afterwards. Then we went home to collect the children from school. William was meant to be playing football, but it was so windy that the match had been cancelled. So we took him and Naomi to a friend's house for tea . . . they were going to swimming club together afterwards.

'I'd been planning to bake cakes that afternoon for the headmaster's retirement party the next day; so I put the oven on, and was busy baking cakes, when the phone rang . . . about a quarter to five. Tim answered it. He said, "I'll come straightaway", and I knew from the tone it was Ken Doran.'

Tim drove to the surgery. He felt he knew what he was going to hear. 'It's always hard to break bad news, especially to a friend. I can't remember Ken's precise words at all . . . just to the effect that it was leukaemia, and the prognosis wasn't good. I can remember asking him what it meant at the worst; and he said the worst would be that William had ten weeks to live.'

CHAPTER 3

As a family doctor, Ken Doran took any form of cancer seriously, and he did not believe in encouraging false optimism. 'I wasn't at all hopeful to Tim. He said, "What's the bottom line?", and I said, "Well, if they don't pull him out of it, it'll be five or ten weeks." But having said that, none of the optimistic things I brought up – that they might be able to pull him out – seemed to change the idea in Tim that William had ten weeks to live. He wanted to know the worst he had to expect. I'm afraid in some respects that's the view I take in medicine in general: if someone wants to know, I won't make it too rosy, because at least then things can only get better.'

Dr Doran arranged for William to be admitted at once to the nearest hospital with specialist facilities – Addenbrooke's, just outside Cambridge. 'And after the trauma of explaining the diagnosis to Tim, I went home, sat back and thought: what would have happened if that had been one of my children?'

As for Tim . . . 'Empty is the only way I can describe how I felt. The only thing I could think of was how I was going to break the news to Sue. I just didn't know how to. Straight out was the only way I could tell her.'

Sue was still at home, baking a second batch of cakes. 'Tim seemed to be gone for ages. I couldn't stand it. I don't want to say, "I knew it was leukaemia," again but I knew it was serious for Ken to phone. I had to phone Mum and Dad. I knew they'd got to come, whatever happened . . . even if Tim came home and William didn't have to go into hospital for a week, I knew I needed them. I phoned Mum up.'

Sue's mother, unlike the rest of the family, calls her by her full name, Susan. 'It was about twenty past five when Susan rang. We hadn't had a word all day. She phoned up and said, "Will you come down and sit with me, Mum?" And her voice was crinkling a little. She wasn't really crying, but she almost was.'

'I can remember Mum's voice broke,' Sue says, when I told her William wasn't well – and you could hear that she was crying. She knew there was something serious, but I don't think I said anything at all except that William was very ill.'

It was not long before Tim was back from Dr Doran's surgery to break the news. 'The thing I knew I'd got to do was stay calm, because I didn't know how Sue would react. She'd had her feelings pent up all day. I'd got to convince her that there was some kind of hope, and that she and I had to be totally contained in order not to panic William. When I got home she was as near hysteria as I have ever seen her.'

'Yes, I was,' Sue agrees. 'I can remember actually pulling my hair while Tim was away. But the minute he got back ... when we'd calmed ourselves, or I'd calmed down, we went upstairs and got out the cases.'

A few minutes later Sue's parents arrived. Having left home in such haste, Sue's mother was surprised at what she found. She had thought that William must have collapsed, that he would be in bed, or at least lying down. She was amazed to discover that William had gone out to tea.

Neville and Jean Poole were shocked by William's diagnosis: 'As far as we were concerned,' Neville Poole says, 'leukaemia was a killer. All the children who'd had leukaemia were dead. Every one I'd known of was dead.'

For Sue the overpowering urge was to hurry. 'After Tim got back from the surgery we were at home for a quarter of an hour, at most. We went upstairs and put a few things in the cases. I phoned Mrs Appleby ... we'd got a lot on the next day, with the headmaster's retirement; it was as though it gave me an excuse for not leaving. I suppose already I was sorting things out, I was trying to organize myself – if you can – for the next day ... or that night, or whatever. And then there were the other children. Fortunately, Naomi was out to tea, like William, and the youngest two had been very good, watching television. I didn't see them from the moment the phone rang till just before we left. We told them William had got something wrong with his blood and had to go into hospital, "and Grandma and Grandad are going to look after you; be good, and we'll be home soon". They hadn't even had tea. And then we picked William up from the friends he was with.'

William remembers that moment. 'Mum came to the door with Dad, and rang the doorbell. I thought: What are you doing here? You're not supposed to be here. And my Dad said, "The blood test's come. We're going for a trip to the hospital."'

Cambridge is fifty-five miles from Terrington St John. Sue drove. 'It gave me something to do. And we both spoke to William. We told him what we'd told the others, that he'd got something wrong with his blood which had to be put right. The journey was a lot better than I expected. The crocuses were out. William was so sweet – I think to some extent he was excited. He said, "Will I have to stay in overnight?" He didn't seem worried . . . he was very chatty. But then he had no reason to be worried. He had no concept of what he was going in for. And it went through my mind as well: This isn't really happening; they've made a dreadful mistake.'

Addenbrooke's is a modern hospital, set in open land two or three miles from Cambridge city centre. William's ward was on the first floor of one of the main blocks. He describes their arrival: 'Mum and Dad and I got the cases and our clothes and things out of the car; and one of the nursery nurses met us and took us up and showed us our room . . . down the corridor and on to the ward. I'd never been in hospital before, except for stitches. I was quite inquisitive, looking round at the ward and the paintings on the walls . . . I could see what the outline was: a very big room with lots of rooms inside it, really.'

Sue followed. Her mind was filled with the idea that this might be William's last walk, that he might never leave the hospital again. During the journey she had been strong. Now that she was actually in the hospital, now that she could smell the atmosphere and see the beds with children in them, she was in danger of breaking down.

'I think we all went into William's room, but I couldn't get out of it again quickly enough, to go to the toilet. On the way I met Mair, the nursery nurse, and had a good old cry with her. I was obviously in a state of shock. I told her what the doctor had said – that we'd possibly only got ten weeks. And she was quite upset by that. "Oh, no," she said, "we do marvellous things here for leukaemia children." I didn't believe her. Basically we went in with no hope. At best, we'd got however many months it turned out to be. At worst, we'd got ten weeks.'

William's room was long and narrow, running from the ward corridor to a window at the far end. Three beds were placed next to each other against the wall to the left of the door – one by the outside window, one in the middle and one by the window into the corridor. William chose the bed by the outside window.

Addenbrooke's is well known for its treatment of leukaemia in children. To the doctors and nurses the initial procedures are routine. William was still feeling perfectly well, but he put on his pyjamas ready to go straight to bed. Shortly afterwards, a doctor came. A needle with a short plastic tube attached to it was inserted into one of the veins on the back of William's hand. The needle was pulled out, and the tube left in place to receive drips or injections. It is a convenient system, although in time the flesh round the catheter can become puffy, in which case a new site has to be found.

'I didn't like it at all,' William says, 'because the needle was so wide – it was a lot harder than an ordinary needle. From then on I was attached to the drip all the time. It was painful when it was first put in – it took a while to get used to, but then it was OK. They wanted samples of urine, blood tests as well, all kinds of things. I was up till midnight. I thought they might have waited till the morning, really.'

For Sue, doctors and nurses could hardly work quickly enough. 'They did everything that first evening: height, weight, urine specimen, stool specimen, physical examination, temperature, pulse, blood pressure, nose swabs, throat swabs, chest X-ray; he had more than one blood test that night – everything except treatment. They couldn't do that until they'd got the diagnosis confirmed.'

Soon after arriving at Addenbrooke's, Sue rang her mother to tell her that William had been admitted. Sue's mother telephoned Tim's brother, Michael, at Welney, and gradually the unwelcome news was passed to other members of the family – to Tim's brothers, Michael and David, and his sister, Ann. It affected Ann deeply. She remembered how twenty years earlier she had nursed a child with leukaemia – a girl the same age as William – and she had died. 'It was at Christmas time. It hit me very hard.'

In Terrington St John, when surgery was over, Ken Doran went to see Sue's mother and father to explain what was wrong with William. He softened his own view of the likely outcome: William could get better, but it would be a long haul. 'They were very worried ... perhaps even more so than Sue and Tim, certainly more tense and anxious. Sue and Tim had things to do. They didn't have time to bite their nails, like the people left at home.'

The story spread rapidly through the village. Sue's mother rang the vicar. Ken Doran had already given the news to his partner, Chris Wood. He passed it on to his wife, Rosemary. She remembers the moment exactly.

'I was standing at the kitchen sink. Chris came home from work and said, "I've got something dreadful to tell you: William's got leukaemia." It was the most awful feeling, because William had been with us a few days before. I'd taken him and our son, Alexei, to the fair – as far as Alexei's concerned, William's his best friend. And William had eaten quite a lot and he seemed fine.

'It was the same sort of feeling I had when my sister-in-law had cancer, and she was pregnant – she died when the baby was three months old. I could feel what Sue was going to go through. My first reaction was to take my pinny off, dry my hands and go down to Sue's house. She wasn't there, which was very frustrating because I desperately wanted to see her.

'In the evening we told Alexei, because he could see something was wrong. We told him William had leukaemia, and I think because of having been involved with my sister-in-law – death is not something that's terribly new to him – he asked, "Is he going to die?" We said, "We don't know. He's very poorly." And Alexei was just very, very quiet.'

Less than an hour after William had been admitted to Addenbrooke's, Dr Jane Tizard, the paediatric registrar in charge of William's case, appeared on the ward. As was the practice on the children's wards at Addenbrooke's, she was informally dressed and wore no white coat. Round her neck was a stethoscope to which clung Roland Rat. A little older than Sue, she was a reassuring presence. She was well aware that many patients believe that a diagnosis of leukaemia amounts to a death sentence. That is a myth which it was her first job to dispel.

'We're not going to say there's no hope. When a child's admitted, we have to reassure parents that, whatever type of leukaemia their child has, there's almost certainly going to be treatment available. For children with the commonest kind of leukaemia, the chances of cure are about eighty per cent. Some people in America quote even higher rates.

'So we have to undertake a number of investigations to see what sort of leukaemia it is, and then we can sit down with the parents and give them a better idea of what the chances are and what the treatment's going to involve. It always seems to help parents accept the terrible shock of the diagnosis if they know that something can be done about it. But we prefer to discuss the details of treatment once we have the results of all the investigations.'

To speak loosely, leukaemia is cancer of the blood. More precisely, 'leukaemia' is the name given to a group of cancers that originate either in the bone-marrow or in the organs associated with the body's immune system, its defences against disease and alien cells. The cancerous cells of the different types of leukaemia show up mainly in the marrow, in the immune system – and in the blood.

When a human egg is fertilized by a sperm, one group of primitive 'stem' cells forms in the yolk sac. These stem cells move into the fetus's liver and then into its developing spleen. Later they seed themselves into the baby's bone-marrow. Once established there, a few weeks before the baby is born, they become the source of two different groups of cells: the lymph cells of the body's immune system, and blood cells.

To achieve this double purpose, the stem cells differentiate themselves along two separate evolutionary trees. Some follow the 'myeloid' tree (so called from the Greek word for marrow), and develop through various immature stages into the different constituents of the blood. Some, for example, eventually turn into red cells which transport oxygen: some become white cells, most of which act as scavengers, fighting and engulfing bacteria; and some become platelets, which prevent internal and external bleeding by acting as a clotting agent. All these blood cells reach maturity in the marrow. They emerge through tiny blood vessels into the bloodstream. They circulate round the body and eventually find their way back into the bone-marrow, only to emerge again.

The lymph cells of the immune system (which play an important part in identifying alien cells and resisting virus diseases) follow a pattern of growth with fewer branches. They emerge from the bone-marrow only partially developed and undergo further change and differentiation in the organs of the lymph system, particularly the thymus, the spleen and the glands. When fully mature they recirculate through the bloodstream and the bone-marrow, ready to respond to alien organisms.

Cancer occurs when the orderly reproduction of different types of cell is interrupted. For some as yet unexplained reason, a single immature cell ignores the feedback mechanism by which the body limits reproduction of cells to the number required. The rogue cell begins reproducing itself without restraint. The identical copies of itself which it creates also ignore the body's control mechanism and begin dividing in their turn. The result is an uncontrolled proliferation of immature cells. The kind of cells they are, and the stage in their evolutionary development which they have reached before going wrong, determine which type of cancer is caused.

In time, such proliferation can produce many thousands of millions of more or less useless cells. Some will be found in the bone-marrow, some may be found in the blood; but they may also colonize and enlarge organs like the spleen (as in William's case), or the liver, or the glands. The damage they do is not simply to clog up different parts of the body's system but also to interfere with the production of normal cells. In time, cancerous cells can virtually eliminate other cells developing in the bone-marrow or the immune system. The consequences are serious. Too few red cells will mean anaemia – loss of energy, paleness, irritability. Too few platelets will mean nose-bleeds, bruising and aching joints from internal bleeding. Too few white blood cells and too few lymph cells in the immune system will result in lack of resistance to infection.

The name 'leukaemia' is derived from Greek words meaning 'white blood'. This is apt when, under a microscope, unnaturally large numbers of immature cells with a whiteish tinge can be detected in the blood. When that happens, doctors refer to 'a high white-cell count'. But a word of warning to the layman is needed. The phrase 'a high white-cell count' does not necessarily imply that the immature cells being observed are precursors of the white blood cells which act as anti-bacterial scavengers. They might be immature forms of other blood cells, or of the different types of cells developed in the body's immune system.

So how much did Jane Tizard, the paediatric registrar, know about what was wrong with William when he reached Addenbrooke's?

'Dr Doran obviously felt that leukaemia was the likely diagnosis. He'd had a routine blood count done locally, and that suggested leukaemia. We're always honest with parents, but we can't make a definite diagnosis until we've done a bone-marrow examination. In William's case, the blood count almost gave us the diagnosis because he had such a high white-cell count. But we needed a bone-marrow test to confirm it, and to tell us the type of leukaemia. We were slightly worried that he might have a myeloid leukaemia, which has a worse prognosis than the commoner lymphoblastic form.'

So there was little specific reassurance Jane Tizard could offer during the first few hours after Willliam was admitted to Addenbrooke's. But she did convince Tim that it was premature to despair.

'From the moment we began to talk to her,' Tim says, 'you were never told anything to make you too optimistic – but you were told just sufficient to make you optimistic enough. With his high white-cell count, William wasn't in the best group of patients . . . but you were made aware how successful treatment is today for the majority of patients.'

Sue recalls how unhurried Dr Tizard appeared: 'She made it seem that she had all the time in the world. I remember going to her room two or three times that first evening; and she would say, "I know you won't take it all in. Just come back and ask. Don't be afraid to ask." You used to learn a little bit at a time. You couldn't take in more than a certain amount each time; but it was always told you again and again until you started to get the picture.'

The observations and tests to which William was subjected immediately after his admission to hospital had specific purposes. The physical examination confirmed the existence of the enlarged spleen and gave an indication of William's general condition. The swabs and specimens would provide evidence of any infections. Taking his temperature would show whether he was feverish. His height and weight would provide a basis for later comparisons. It seemed that William was not particularly unwell in himself, which gave him a better chance of withstanding any treatment. Dr Tizard was pleased.

'We took a lot of blood samples so that our haematologists could confirm that there was a high white-cell count. But often in leukaemia the red-cell count is low as well. That could mean a blood transfusion. That's part of the treatment which you can start right away, before the full diagnosis is made. In fact William's haemoglobin level (reflecting his red-cell count) was low, but not low enough to need a transfusion that night.

'William also had a chest X-ray – that's all part of the routine for anyone suspected of having leukaemia. There are several things that we look for. If someone has a low red-cell count and is very anaemic, and it's been going on for some time, the heart may have become enlarged from the extra stress of pumping enough blood to supply the tissues with oxygen. If it has, we have to be very careful when we transfuse blood.

'We also look for lung infections on the X-ray. Children with leukaemia are very prone to infection, particularly odd types of infection. Occasionally the leukaemic cells themselves can infiltrate the lungs, but that's rare. William had a temperature when he came in; so we needed to make sure there was no evidence of infection in his lungs. But you can't always find the cause of a fever, so we always treat patients with antibiotics, blindly to begin with, until we have the results of the cultures we get from the swabs, which may take several days. That's because the white blood cells (which normally fight infection) are abnormal in patients with leukaemia and can't work efficiently. So even if we don't grow any bacteria from the swabs, it's safer to treat with antibiotics immediately. We gave William antibiotics through his drip.'

Sue settled William down to sleep soon after midnight: 'Tim and I slept in his room. When we were admitted, there were two beds in the room as well as William's – that was a tremendous relief. Right from the start we could sleep in his room. For me, that softened some of the blow. You knew you didn't have to get into your car and drive away – go home and leave William there. To begin with, I had visions that we'd have to find somewhere to stay – outside the hospital, but not too far away. Tim and I thought about spending the night with friends in Cambridge. But to stay in his room, both of us, was a great comfort – that you could all be together.'

Tim adds: 'The only other thing I can clearly remember thinking that night was that, whatever happened, I'd got to sleep. To me, Sue looked as if she wasn't going to.'

'I didn't,' Sue says. 'I tried to. I lay down, but the minute I lay down, I was up. Tim rolled over and made up his mind that he'd got to go to sleep – Tim very much needs his sleep. But I would have gone mad. I would have gone crazy. I just lay down and thought: try and go to sleep; and then I'd sit straight up because I knew there was no way . . . and I'd try again. Then I'd just look at William, who would be fast asleep. It's a strange thing, a hospital – the first night, anyway. I can remember feeling . . . not cross . . . I suppose it *was* kind of cross, that Tim could lie there and go to sleep. All this was happening, I needed to talk to him, and he just lay there. I don't think he had a particularly good night . . . but he did sleep. We had single beds, they weren't pushed together, and he just turned his back to me and closed his eyes.

'I kept trying to lie down. But I couldn't. I didn't know where to go or quite what to do, but I just knew I'd got to stand up. I suppose it was a kind of claustrophobia . . . I was going to scream. I can remember going outside the door, and the nurses' desk was just opposite; I found myself just drifting there and . . . the tears were coming . . . and they just pulled up a chair, and I sat with them all night. They weren't that busy during the night. And I just talked to them all night about William. But I can remember laughing. You know, I'd suddenly cry,

I'd have a cup of coffee, and we'd be laughing. We had quite a party, in a funny kind of way. I don't think I went back in the room any more, and Tim didn't come out.

'I can't ever remember feeling like that before. The nurses are obviously used to it; but they didn't give me any hope. I wanted them to say, "William will be all right", but they couldn't. They didn't know anything.

'And then day came . . . the birds singing and the light coming. I've never been so grateful to see the dawn – everything coming back to life, I suppose. I can remember being on the phone to my mother at six o'clock that first morning and talking to her. I knew she'd be up. She said, "Are you sure he's got leukaemia?", and I said "Yes"; and then Ann – Tim's sister, Ann – arrived. She was working at Addenbrooke's, just by coincidence, on a course. I was capable of talking to my mother quite well, until I saw Ann.'

Ann had come in early to see Sue, before beginning her shift. 'I wasn't on duty till half past seven. I just took one look at Sue and we both burst into tears. Really, we couldn't talk. We just dissolved into tears and that was it.'

'Yes,' Sue explained, 'because she was the first person from home I'd seen.'

CHAPTER 4

If Sue did not sleep the first night that William was in hospital, neither did her parents. Neville and Jean Poole, having given the two younger children their tea before Naomi returned and tucked them all up in their own beds upstairs, sat up till dawn, making one pot of tea after another.

William was their eldest grandchild. He was certainly the one Neville knew best.

'When he was younger, he used to spend a lot of time on the farm. I took William miles on the tractor. Every Sunday I used to take William on the tractor; you were allowed to do that then. He would actually come on the fields while you were ploughing, on the crawler. You can't do that now, but I wouldn't say it's dangerous. Machinery's predictable. The reason more people get hurt on farms is that they don't learn young enough to get out of the way. What they learn when they're young, they never forget. You can't learn how to drive tractors and that sort of thing at college. Of course, you can't trust children with horses. If you say "Whoa" to a horse and it doesn't, you're in trouble.'

Neville and Jean's farm was not far from Sue and Tim's house. It lay half a mile from the village crossroads along the main road to Wisbech. Every day, soon after half past seven, Neville used to drive over in his van to say "Good morning" and spend a few minutes chatting. On Saturdays he would often bring the children something from the village shop.

Neville and Jean were close to the younger children. They often babysat; and it was not surprising that they should be available to take charge overnight when William was taken to hospital – an arrangement which was to last. When Jean first rang Tim's family to give them the news of William's illness, Tim's family offered to help with the younger children, but Jean was clear about what she wanted done: she would cope with the children, if Tim's family would visit William in hospital.

Sue knew such a deal would suit the children. 'They were very used to my parents; there weren't many days when they didn't see them . . . and they were able to stay in their own home for a lot of the time. My parents have the same habits and way of looking after people as we have, because we live nearby and see each other often enough to know exactly. They didn't always quite approve of what I was doing; but Mum knew where school was, how I dressed the children for school, and what food they ate. And she knew the house. She was able to prepare a meal, and knew where to find a change of sheets and the children's clothes. In fact, when I came home, it wasn't my home any more. It was my mother's, and she knew better than I did where everything was. So the children were very lucky that Mum and Dad did move in.'

When Naomi, Harriet and Edward arrived at the village school on the day after William's diagnosis, they were greeted by the familiar figure of Mrs Appleby. It was the last day of the Easter term.

The village school is not a Church school. The vicar, having three parishes, does not teach there every week, but that afternoon he was taking assembly to mark the headmaster's retirement. William's name was included in the prayers.

'I think the village was shocked by the news about William,' Mrs Appleby says. 'There was a tremendous amount of feeling. It's difficult to explain, but we were reeling. I'd never experienced an intensity of feeling like there was in the village – but then I don't come from a small village, I come from Wolverhampton. The night before, the Monday, I had been to swimming club and had told everybody there. Next day my youngest son said to me that William had swum for them at the gala when he was obviously very ill; William hadn't let them down, and they weren't going to let William down. The top swimmers, the ones who swim every night, decided they wanted to do something. They said, "We're going to do a twenty-four-hour sponsored swim for leukaemia research."'

In Addenbrooke's, William had slept through the night. 'The ward was quite quiet. By nine o'clock the next morning I was just coming round. I didn't want any breakfast, I felt so bad. I just didn't feel like eating, in the situation I was in.'

This was perhaps just as well, since it was in any case necessary for William to go without food in preparation for the next stage of the investigations. He was due to give a sample of bone-marrow and have a lumbar puncture. It was something that could be done on the ward by Jane Tizard and her colleagues, but to Sue and Tim it seemed like a full-scale operation, the first big test.

Tim was relieved by William's reaction. 'William just accepted it.

He said, "I know it's going to make me well." It wasn't, "You can do anything to me: I don't mind." He wanted to know what they were going to do, and why; he was interested. But he had total faith.'

William was taken into the treatment-room, and given a short-acting general anaesthetic through his drip. When he was fully unconscious, he was turned on to his side with his knees drawn up, so that the bones of his spine showed up through the skin. A needle was then inserted between two of the vertebrae of his spine into the fluid that surrounds the spinal cord. A few drops of the fluid were collected for analysis. Afterwards Jane Tizard gave William an injection, also into the spinal fluid.

'The lumbar puncture was necessary,' she explained, 'because in leukaemia you can get leukaemic cells, malignant cells, infiltrating the spinal fluid. That only happens in a small number of children, but it carries a worse prognosis, so we took a sample of the fluid to find out whether there were leukaemic cells there or not.

'The injection (together with radiotherapy later) was designed to kill any leukaemic cells that might have escaped into the spinal fluid or the fluid surrounding the brain. Even though we hadn't had time to analyse the sample, we still went ahead and gave William an injection because it is very important to give prophylactic treatment to stop leukaemic cells spreading into the central nervous system.'

The second stage of the operation was to take a sample of William's bone-marrow.

The picture of human marrow evoked by recollections of the marrow-bones on sale in butchers' shops is misleading. Human bone-marrow is not a jelly. In the form in which a sample is collected, it is a fluid. Essentially it is a congregation of immature cells in various stages of development. But these immature cells are also mingled with the mature cells which circulate round the main bloodstream back into the bone-marrow cavities, and then out into the bloodstream again. As a result, bone-marrow, when extracted, looks very like blood.

Bone-marrow is found in a number of large bones in the human skeleton, but the largest and most accessible source is the hip bone, or pelvis. To take a bone-marrow sample from William, Dr Tizard and her colleagues laid him on his side on the operating table, leaving just his hips uncovered. She then inserted a large needle into the flat part of the hip-bone at the bottom of William's spine, and drew out a few millilitres of bone-marrow. In Addenbrooke's, collecting bone-marrow samples is a matter of routine, and the whole procedure was over in a few minutes.

Dr Tizard sent the sample of bone-marrow to the hospital laboratories, where tiny droplets were smeared on to slides, which were then looked at under the microscope by the haematologists.

'The specific diagnosis of the type of leukaemia is always made on the bone-marrow examination,' Dr Tizard explained, 'because leukaemia is a cancer of white cells which starts off in the bone-marrow; so even if no leukaemic cells have spilled out into the bloodstream, there will always be leukaemic cells in the marrow. Actually William did have a very high white-cell count in his blood, and sometimes you can tell what kind of leukaemia it is by looking at those cells; but we still try and do more specific tests on the bone-marrow cells.'

Sue and Tim were excluded from the treatment-room while William was under the anaesthetic. Tim took the opportunity to telephone his assistant, Claire Shewring, at work in the shop.

Claire had known both Tim and Sue for many years: 'I'd known them since they were teenagers, in fact – half their lives. I went to their wedding. I can remember the first time I held William. He was very tiny – only ten or eleven days old. He was perfect. Since then I've known them all the way through. I've worked for Tim since 1980, when he came to King's Lynn to the new shop . . . my function is admin., paperwork, keeping the books straight, keeping the shop going, pretty well everything except the buying.

'Well, on the Tuesday, Tim phoned and said "We're in Addenbrooke's. William's got leukaemia. It's very serious. You're running the ship." I said, "Fine," and I asked him if he wanted me to tell people. He said, "No, play it cool for the time being. Just say William's not well, until we know more definitely."

'It was a terrible shock. When I put the phone down, I went to tell my husband and I just burst into tears. But after the initial explosion, we just got on with the rest of the day. It was very calmly done. I thought: this is what's expected of me. This is what I'm going to do.'

William's operations were over by the middle of the morning. When he got back to his room and began to recover, he was dozy but not ill. A layman might expect both a lumbar puncture and the extraction of bone-marrow to have painful after-effects. In fact, neither left William feeling any worse than a little stiff and sore. More difficult was the adjustment to life in a hospital, not only for William, but for his parents.

For Sue, the day seemed very busy. 'It didn't drag. I wonder now if we were still in such a state of shock that we were just stunned by it all, but we didn't sit there with nothing happening. There were things like going for an X-ray – an hour and a half by the time the porter had got you there and back. William was in the wheelchair, and one of us was pushing the drip beside him on its frame, on castors; and a student nurse always came with us.

'I shall never forget the bleep on his drip in his room. It was like a life-and-death situation: if the machine didn't work, William was going to die . . . as though he was on a life-support machine. It was all right while the machine was working, but the minute the red light came on – and there were times when the drip didn't quite work and they had to cancel it and sort it out – then you used to panic. The nurses were in pretty quickly, and it was usually just air in the line . . . but you'd think: Air in the line's dangerous. In fact it was simply a drip with saline solution to keep his body fluids up, and some antibiotics.

'And then we were doing things like getting William to watch the video, and organizing food. The nursery nurse brought in some games, and we played Cluedo.'

As the day wore on, it became clearer what William's stay in hospital was going to mean. Despite his visits to the treatment-room and the X-ray department, the hospital's policy was to keep leukaemia patients in isolation. This was not because leukaemia is infectious – it is not – but because leukaemia makes them vulnerable to outside infection. The multiplying cancer cells interfere with the reproduction of the normal marrow cells which help to defend the body against disease. They crowd out, as it were, the healthy white cells of the blood and the immune system. So leukaemia patients have to be kept in an environment that is as clean and free from infection as possible.

This meant that William himself had to stay in his room. He was not to leave either to wash or to go to the lavatory, although at the time he was admitted he was quite strong enough. Almost the only people allowed into his room were nurses, doctors and his parents. Raw food was forbidden; all his food had to be cooked or come out of a sealed packet or tin. Drinks were from sealed boxes, cans or bottles. The hospital provided cooked food, but William, like most of the leukaemia patients, did not want to eat it. He was not hungry; neither was Sue. 'Tim and I had by this time found our way to the hospital shop, and we were forcing the odd thing down – an occasional bread roll. But we cooked for William separately. There was a little kitchen with a microwave oven and a Baby Belling. But he didn't eat anything.'

During the day, Tim's elder brother, Michael, came over from the farm at Welney. It was the first of many family visits. Tuesday also brought the regular clinic at which children who had been victims of leukaemia came back for a check-up. Sue could hardly avoid meeting them, and these encounters were a revelation.

'Not knowing anything about leukaemia, I automatically presumed that the majority of children died. I realized very quickly at the clinic that there were an awful lot of children two years on, four years on, still running around, and that they looked perfectly normal. I don't know how I expected they were going to look, but you wouldn't have known there was anything wrong with them. And the parents encouraged me: "Don't give up hope. Two years ago it was my son. Now look at him."'

What turns out well for other people's children may not, however, turn out well for your own. Sue and Tim could draw general comfort from the survival of the children they saw, but that could not give them any assurance about William. All they knew about him was that he was the victim of an aggressive cancer and that he was beginning to feel the effects. From time to time he would need blood transfusions; but he was not at this time receiving any active treatment, and the type of leukaemia was not yet known.

By Tuesday night some of the bone-marrow tests carried out in the hospital's own laboratories had been completed. The evidence they provided was enough to make Dr Tizard almost certain of the diagnosis. She gave the news to Sue.

'On the Tuesday night,' Sue says, 'Jane Tizard said she was ninety-nine per cent sure it was the commonest type of leukaemia – and that's not the worst type. Suddenly that one per cent of uncertainty became terribly important.'

The diagnosis could only be confirmed by further tests carried out in London, at the Hospital for Sick Children in Great Ormond Street. Desperate to do something positive to help, Tim volunteered to drive the samples to London, but his offer was refused.

Sue was venting her anxiety in a different way. 'I'd been talking non-stop all that day. I was completely whacked, exhausted with talking. That's how I coped. That night the nurses offered me a sleeping tablet at eleven o'clock, but I didn't take it. Then in the early hours of that second night, three or four o'clock, I was suddenly beginning to feel tired. I thought: Perhaps if I have a sleeping tablet now, I might go to sleep. And I did. Within half an hour I was sleeping well.

'But I can remember taking that tablet, sitting with the nurses. For once I didn't drink any coffee. I was so sick of coffee. My coffee-drinking started the minute I took William back to school after Ken Doran had seen him. I ate nothing that day. I had coffee at school. I went to Tim: Claire was there, making me coffee. I went to the hairdresser: she made me a coffee. Then I was given another great mug of coffee by the friend who was having William and Naomi for tea – I told her what the doctor had said, because I couldn't really hide it from anyone I saw. The coffee didn't go down very well, but when I got home and started baking, I automatically made another coffee. And they made us coffee when we arrived at Addenbrooke's. I can remember for three or four days I didn't touch coffee after that.'

Next day, Wednesday, William was beginning to look and feel less and less well. He began to be sick. He had stomach-ache. Sue watched him anxiously. 'He had flannels on his head, and flannels on his tummy – and three extractor fans going. It was hot, but he was obviously feverish. He was very poorly, and I knew anyone walking past could only think what an ill little boy he looked.'

'He developed tummy pain early on,' said Dr Tizard. 'First of all we thought it was over the spleen – an acutely enlarged spleen can be painful. But then the pain seemed to be lower down. He had a bit of diarrhoea. We do worry about infections in the gut, and that was one reason why we gave him antibiotics in the first few days.'

Sue found that she and Tim needed to do some shopping for William in Cambridge. Tim's brother, Michael, had come over again from Welney, and could keep William company. 'We bought him a new dressing-gown, two pairs of pjyamas – we'd brought towelling ones, and all the things we'd packed were far too hot for hospital . . . our room was unbearably hot, over the boilers. And we got him a set of darts. He'd been on about a real dartboard for ages. He actually mentioned it on the way to Addenbrooke's. These were little miniature darts. I remember we spent forty pounds that day. Money didn't matter. We were buying for William – nothing but the best. We didn't even think of asking the price.'

Still there was a delay in establishing exactly what type of leukaemia William had; and still no treatment.

That night Sue went home for the first time to collect a few necessaries for a longer stay in hospital. Instead of driving herself or getting Tim to drive her, she enlisted the help of the family.

'Ann came off her shift at Addenbrooke's at half past seven. I thought I'd go back with her to Welney House, get a lift on home, pick up a few bits and pieces, and be back in hospital next morning. Ann's husband, Mick, took me on from Welney to Terrington St John. That was very late, about half past eleven. Then it turned out that Naomi had been feeling sick. I felt I'd better not risk seeing her and taking any infection back to William. So I went back and slept at Mick and Ann's at Welney. I didn't even go and see the children asleep in bed. I won't say I didn't want to, but I thought: no, I've got to move. I'd just as well not see the children.' I almost forgot the things I'd come for. I didn't even talk to Mum and Dad properly.

'I got to bed about half past one in the morning. I had two rounds of cheese on toast, and coffee with brandy in it. That was the first time I'd really eaten since Monday. And I remember, I had a cry and then went out like a light. The next thing I knew, it was seven o'clock the next morning.'

On the fourth day of William's stay in Addenbrooke's the results of the bone-marrow tests carried out at Great Ormond Street were relayed to Cambridge. Dr Tizard was pleased. It was, she said, basically good news. 'Initially we were worried that William might have one of the rarer leukaemias, a myeloid leukaemia. But Great Ormond Street were definite that it was the commonest form of leukaemia, a lymphocytic leukaemia. That's a leukaemia of the immature lymphocytes, known as acute lymphoblastic leukaemia, or ALL. And that has the best prognosis.

'William's blood was quite difficult to analyse. Different types of white cells have different surface markers. You can make specific antibodies which identify these markers and attach themselves to the appropriate cells. The antibodies can be labelled, so that under a microscope different types of cells show up differently. But sometimes there's a mixed reaction – that's what happened in William's case, when we analysed the samples at Addenbrooke's. Great Ormond Street were able to establish not only that it was the commonest form of leukaemia with the best outlook, but that within that form it was the commonest type of cells that were affected. Again, that gave a better outlook.

'So far as William's chances went, we were pleased he had lymphoblastic leukaemia as opposed to myeloid, which we hadn't known for certain the day before; and it was also the common sort of lymphoblastic leukaemia. Balancing that was the fact that William had a very high white-cell count initially, which meant that it was an aggressive form of the disease.

'These days, of the group with the best prognosis, seventy to eighty per cent survive. With William we had to cut that down a bit. He had about a fifty per cent chance of survival.'

At the time, talking to Sue, Dr Tizard did not put a figure on William's chances.

'Jane put it very simply,' said Sue. 'You can think of leukaemia as either white, grey or black. When William was admitted, Tim and I thought he was in the black area. It turned out he was in the grey. He couldn't go into the white, even though he had A L L, because he had such a high white-cell count, and he was a nine-year-old boy – if he'd been a nine-year-old girl, it wouldn't have been so bad, because girls tend to do better. So William came in the grey area – and that was quite a relief.'

That night, William's treatment began.

CHAPTER 5

William's treatment at Addenbrooke's depended on drugs – chemotherapy, as the doctors call it. The aim was to destroy all the cancerous cells, so that normal cells could develop and multiply again. The difficulty was to eliminate the cancerous cells from his blood, his bone-marrow and his immune system without eliminating all other cells as well. The drugs used were powerful and dangerous. The very adjective doctors use to describe them, cytotoxic, means 'poisonous to cells'. But Jane Tizard took the view that William's very high white-cell count was an unfavourable sign, and made it necessary to prescribe the heaviest schedule of treatment available.

She explained the regime that would be adopted: 'We have an established treatment, which is the best known treatment. However, we're trying to improve it all the time. There are national trials going on up and down the country in which variations on the established treatment are compared with it to see if the results are better. People have been doing pilot studies into giving extra blocks of treatment. The advantage is that you may have a better chance of getting rid of the leukaemia; on the other hand, you may run a greater risk of side-effects. And because the treatment of leukaemia is in any case so good these days, we don't want to cause more illness or more deaths from the treatment we give.

'So we allocate children to the different regimes randomly – we could toss a coin, but we use a computer. At the end of about a five-year period we analyse the results; but if at any time it becomes clear that one regime is much better, then obviously the trial would be stopped and that regime used.

'When we have a case where some factors indicate a worse outlook, we obviously opt for a more intensive treatment. In that case we don't allocate a child randomly. We say: "You're going to get the most intensive treatment", and we take the extra risks of side-effects and infection. However, we have to say that we don't yet know if more treatment is necessarily better treatment.

'In William's case, for the first two days the drugs were given via the drip into his vein – he already had a drip up, for antibiotics and blood transfusions. He then had a course of drugs by mouth, steroid tablets, over a period of weeks. He also had a course of injections into his leg – nine injections over three weeks – and a separate course of weekly injections into the vein. Every fortnight he had a lumbar puncture and a bone-marrow test to check what was going on. Then, in this particular schedule, after four weeks he had another very intensive course of treatment over five days.

'All the drugs we gave have some way of stopping the replication of the leukaemic cells – preventing the genetic material in the cells splitting. The danger is that they don't simply affect leukaemic cells; they tend to affect any cells that are dividing. That's why they make your hair fall out – they stop the hair cells dividing. Again, in the mouth and the gut the mucous membranes are made up of cells that divide quickly. So the drugs affect them, and you can get mouth-ulcers. And if there are any normal cells in the bone-marrow, you're stopping them dividing as well. Not only the bad cells, but also the good cells are affected.

'Of course, you don't wipe out absolutely everything in the bone-marrow, because if you wipe out everything, and there are none of the original, primitive, 'stem' cells left, then the patient doesn't start to produce any replacement cells at all. The treatment we give aims to leave some primitive cells lower down the development chain which can eventually diversify and multiply into the different kinds of mature cells.'

William's injections were not administered directly, but through the permanent tube on the back of his hand, which was also used for drips and transfusions. For Tim, watching was not pleasant: 'It was like injecting acid – it burned; and it was a big injection, a big syringe – sixty mils.'

Sue knew that it was painful because, unusually for him, William complained. 'He would cry out that it was stinging, and then they would inject it so it went through slowly. I'm sure they added saline as well, to help flush it – it was on a two-way tap, going into the back of his hand, a "butterfly" catheter.'

Caution was required at all times, as Dr Tizard was well aware. 'We have to be very careful that the drugs we put into the drip go into the vein and not round the outside, because you can get nasty burns from the drugs if they get under the skin. And that's why we wear gowns when we draw up the drugs, and glasses to stop them getting into our eyes. They're toxic drugs.'

But Sue felt that the chemotherapy was making William feel better

– 'Initially it did seem to make him feel better. He had been very poorly. I didn't know why; I thought it was the leukaemia taking hold. For the two days before the chemotherapy, he was sick. I can remember going down to X-ray and he would be very sick. And he used to be sick in his room. I think the chemotherapy stopped that . . . because his spleen went down fairly quickly, and therefore the tummy-ache went. But one of the side-effects of the treatment is constipation; and after a day or two he had a terrific problem with that. He was doubled up with pain sometimes, just as he had been before the treatment started. I pictured he'd have to have his appendix out, and all sorts of things.'

On Saturday morning William was watching television in his room; later he recalled how he had learnt about leukaemia, in a quite unexpected way.

'They said on the TV, "Right, we're going to do a survey or something for leukaemia research; and we want you to make up a song and write in with it – perhaps with a tape of you singing it and playing it. The best four families will come on the show with the Minipops, and the winner will get this organ." They were going to produce a record of the person who won and put it in the shops, and all the money would go towards leukaemia research; but they made a record with all four songs on because they were so good.

'They were going on about: "Leukaemia is a cancer of the blood." That's how I found out that I had cancer. Having leukaemia and wondering what they were on about, I suddenly heard the word "cancer", and that meant something to me. I turned to Mum and said, "I didn't know leukaemia was a cancer." And she said, "We've never got round to telling you." It was quite hard, thinking I had cancer. Grandpa had died of cancer a few months back; so I realized that cancer could kill people.'

The question of how to tell William he had cancer had been worrying Tim and Sue for some time, and Sue was quite alarmed when the programme started. 'There was no warning of what was coming. They wouldn't think of a child in hospital, newly diagnosed, finding out in that way what was wrong with him. There it was: "Leukaemia is a cancer of the blood." And he heard before I could stop him. I instantly said, "Shall I switch it off?" And he replied, "No, I want to watch it", and he watched it, and was very intent on watching it. And then of course we had to go through the whole thing: "You can die of leukaemia. But there's a lot of treatment, and that can make you better."'

Later Tim discussed the programme with William, and told him there was a possibility he might die. William was prepared. 'He knew that if he did die, he would go straight to heaven. But I don't think he considered he was going to die any more than the rest of us consider that we're going to die. You don't sit and contemplate, and I don't think William, although he's very mature for his age, would sit and contemplate something like that in depth.'

It was a situation that Dr Tizard recognized. She realized that it was a very low moment for William. She and her colleagues spent some time talking to him about it. Up to that point William hadn't asked very many questions; when the possibility of dying came out in the open, he talked about it more. 'It's very difficult,' Dr Tizard comments, 'to broach that subject and talk about dying with a child who hasn't talked about it. But it may be something he's worrying about.'

Though Sue felt William needed to know that he could die from leukaemia, it had some awkward consequences. 'We tried to tell him that you can die from it, but to reassure him that he wouldn't die. What would happen, though, if we suddenly found out that something was going wrong? He was going to ask, "Am I going to die?" Would we then be able to turn round and say, "You won't die"? I didn't know.'

Dr Tizard said: 'From the doctor's point of view, I think children worry more about the treatment they're going to have – whether it's going to hurt them. But William's age-group is very difficult. He was mature, but he was also still a child. With three- and four-year-olds you're not going to have that kind of conversation – although you'd be amazed how astute some children are.'

After William had watched the programme, Sue felt that she had nothing else to tell him. 'He now knew everything. I'd told him almost straight away that he'd got leukaemia – not that it meant anything to him. Then I'd told him what leukaemia was, that it was a blood disorder, and that he'd feel sick and lose his hair during the treatment – and that was another couple of days; you let that sink in. Telling him it was cancer was the hard part, but after the programme I felt nothing was hidden at all. It was cancer. It took the day for it to sink in. He was very quiet – very, very quiet. And then, no problem. He knew you could die.'

Late that evening, Sue went home for the night. Surprisingly, after less than a week at Addenbrooke's, it was becoming difficult to break out of hospital routine. 'I wanted to see the children, but I didn't want the hassle of being pestered for attention by them. They were already asleep when I got back, but I knew they'd all be demanding to sit next to me at breakfast in the morning. I had to go home anyway, though, to fill Mum and Dad in.'

Next day was Easter, and Sue got up early to go to church.

'I can remember at Easter, when I went to church, people couldn't understand why I'd gone. Yet that's really why I came home. I wanted – I *needed* to go to church. I didn't want to be there at the beginning of the service – I didn't want to walk in with everyone else. I just wanted to creep in at the back. I knew how the latch worked on the door, and I was careful not to make a noise. And the very first words I heard were ". . . pray for William Clayton".

'My mother wasn't like me. She told Mrs Appleby she'd go to church when she had something to be thankful for. "When William rings and says 'Hullo, Grandma', I shall know he's better. I shall go to church when I have something to be thankful for. I can't go yet."

'My faith did give me tremendous strength. I went to chapel every day that week at the hospital. And I felt the strength take over on the second or third day that William was ill. It took a couple of days, and then I suddenly decided that I could fight, and that I'd got to cope with it all.

'Each thing that happened, I used to pray. Tim was at the doctor's: "Please, God, don't let it be leukaemia." But it was. I mean, God let me down. And then, when Tim came back from the doctor's: "Please, God, give me strength to cope." And I can remember going to the toilet and saying, "Please, God, help us." And when we got to the hospital, and all through that night and the next day, it was: "Please, God." Actually it was "Don't let it be that", first; and then afterwards "Help us."

'The night Tim came back from the doctor's and said that William had leukaemia, I said to Tim, "I wish William had been killed on the way home from school." Having watched father-in-law suffer, how could I watch William suffer? How could we go through it all again? But then after the first week, I was so pleased that we'd had that week with him. It gave us so much. Every day, literally every day, you were grateful for. There were times when Tim and I thought: can we just get through another day, another day we've had with our little boy? But as Tim said, we all die, and it's only a question of time. The prayer was not just "Let William live", but accepting that the answer might be "No". That was the hard part.

'There was always someone worse off than we were. During that first week, there was a little girl who was abducted. It was on television – we had a TV set, and we were beginning to take notice of the outside world again – and it was the first thing that caught my attention. Her mother didn't even know where she was. I could relate to that mother . . . what she was going through. Everyone assumed the little girl would be found dead, but her mother didn't know. At least we knew where William was, even if he was going to die. And there was hope for us. We were building up hope day by day.

'For the first few days, I couldn't help asking, "Why us?" We hadn't neglected William or deprived him of anything. That was one thing I thought: if anything happened to him, we had given him everything, he'd never gone without anything. And why William? He'd always been a good boy – not that the others are that dreadful – and he was academically bright. I couldn't understand *why*. I wouldn't have wished it on the other three children, but I couldn't work out why it should be William. But it wasn't long – by the end of the week – that I decided it was because William could cope with it. He had the character, he never complained.'

The early communion service ended about nine o'clock. Sue drove a few hundred yards along the road to the farmhouse where Chris and Rosemary Wood lived.

'I came out of church,' said Sue, 'and I can remember I didn't want to go home. I wanted to talk to someone. But I didn't want to worry my mother. I went along to Rosemary's, and at first I thought there was nobody up. And then she appeared at the window in her dressing-gown and I went in.

'Of course, after William went into Addenbrooke's we got help from absolutely everyone, not just from friends and people we knew well. People we would never have imagined were offering to help with looking after the children, or to do anything they could. But Rosemary was one of the friends I had most in common with – and I felt she had a feeling for William.'

Rosemary, too, has a clear recollection of that morning. 'I can remember Sue sitting there, very vividly. I was amazed how well she was coping and how well she talked about it, about her fears and what might happen. Obviously, she needed someone to talk to outside the family. It sounds a bit silly, but I'd just recently become involved in hospices for the dying, with a Swiss psychiatrist who's spent all her life with people who are dying, adults and children; and I suddenly

41

thought: Is this why I've got involved in the hospice business? – as if it had given me something that people could plug in to.'

For William's younger brother and his two sisters, Sue and Tim's departure had been very sudden. Naomi, the eldest of the three children left with their grandparents, had not even been at home when William was taken away to Addenbrooke's: 'I was at my friend Kelly's for tea. William was there, too, with Daniel. They were going swimming. What had happened was: Mum came round and said, "Come on, William. It's time for you to go to hospital. Grandma will pick Naomi up later." So I stayed at Kelly's about three hours longer. When I got home, Grandma said, "Mum and Dad would have been at Addenbrooke's two hours ago!" About three days later we had a phone call saying William had leukaemia.'

Naomi vividly recalls the dislocation caused by the suddenness of William's illness, and the pleasure of seeing Sue again at Easter. But perhaps her memory magnifies the details! 'We were glad to see that someone had come home at the weekend. They did jobs like the last washing-up before William was ill – they hadn't washed-up before William was ill. About four days later, Mum came home to do the washing-up.'

Sue did not stay at home for long. She wanted to get back to William in Cambridge. Meanwhile other people had been thinking about him, too, including Mrs Appleby, his teacher.

'On the Thursday night, at swimming club, they'd collected over thirty pounds in one evening, just from the few parents who were there. They asked me what I thought William would like. We decided amongst ourselves that as he couldn't take his piano, we'd buy him an electronic keyboard. One of the mums bought the keyboard and I took it down to William's Grandma's on Easter Sunday afternoon. The other three children were finding life quite fun. It was great, and probably quite exciting. They were seeing all these people, and doing all these nice exciting things, and being spoilt. Sue said they'd never known what bubble gum was like till William went into hospital. Life was far from mundane.

'I took the keyboard down about two o'clock. Their Grandma was looking tired, and I said, "Well, I'll take the children." She asked which child I would take, and I said, "I can't take just one. It'll have to be all three." So Edward ran round in the garden, and the girls made cakes with Rebecca, my daughter . . . Rebecca and I always bake on Sundays. We must have made three or four dozen. We took them back to Grandma's – they were the most lurid orange and pink. I think most of them fed the birds in the end.'

CHAPTER 6

Sue was not the only member of the family to need support. To the casual observer Tim appeared calm and self-possessed, but the rest of the family soon realized the strain he was under. His sister, Ann, working at Addenbrooke's herself, saw him frequently, and wondered how he would cope. 'Pa's death hit him very hard. William's illness could have been the last straw. He was very tense, and you couldn't really get close to him; for a time it was almost as if there was a brick wall round him.'

Tim didn't want to let himself go, because if he did, he didn't quite know what the results would be. 'The first time I went home, to see how the children were getting on with their grandparents, Neville said the same thing. He cooked my tea, and he said to me, "The only thing you and I can do is just not crack." He and I had a very emotional evening together, which we both needed. I just knew in my own mind that, no matter what I did, I couldn't allow myself to crack. I knew it would be like a dam breaking and there would be no way of holding it back. I think that was what Neville was fighting the whole time, too. I felt quite different after that evening. And I don't think that Neville ever cracked, either. I know he didn't go to bed for two or three nights. He sat up in the chair all night, chain-smoking, I'm sure, with one cup of tea followed by another, drowning himself in tannin.'

Neville felt that he had to keep going for the sake of the children. 'Grandma and I, we were so used to them, it didn't make all that difference. But it was hard . . . when you've got someone with an illness like that – knowing what it was – to have three children jumping up and down and playing up one way or another. You couldn't say to them, "Be quiet; I've got something to think about." We couldn't let them see that. Yet you couldn't tell them everything in the garden was lovely. Grandma worried that perhaps we didn't cope with the children as well as Susan would have normally. But they didn't seem to mind being left. They didn't really play up.'

If Neville and Jean were fond of the children, the children returned the affection, as Naomi testifies. 'Grandma's kind. And before William was ill, Grandad used to bring us a packet of sweets every Saturday.

He gave us pound coins about once a month. He used to come down to our house every morning during the week, but he didn't usually come on Sundays because we went to see him on Sunday afternoons. Grandma picks us up on her way to church every Sunday, and we used to go to hers for tea, with radish and lettuce – and nice things as well.'

Neville and Jean's house, like the farm, was kept in beautiful order. It was probably as old as Tim and Sue's house, but over the years any old-world elements had been subordinated to serviceability and good building practice. Beams were plastered over and corners squared off. As Tim could not help noticing enviously, there was no rising damp. The furniture was modern.

Naomi noticed other distinctive features. 'Grandma's house is up the main road – where we get petrol, and chips. It's different from our house. The bedrooms are definitely different . . . we've got one more bedroom. When we are at Grandma's, Edward sleeps in a big double bed. Me and Harriet sleep in two different beds next to each other. At home we have duvets, but at Grandma's we had five heavy blankets.

'The kitchen's about as big as half our kitchen, big enough for two people. So if we're there, we have to eat in the conservatory or the TV room . . . that's about as big as our dining-room. But you can cook in the kitchen. You can put a sack of potatoes in one corner – and there's a little space under the draining-board, and we put things under there. And there's a cupboard with all the dry stuff, and a cupboard with the saucepans in.

'We helped sometimes with the drying-up. Sometimes we made the beds. Grandma was quite strict. One day of the week we had to help her, on the day we hadn't got anything else to do. I was usually out on Thursday for piano; Harriet's usually out on Tuesday, so I did Tuesday, she did Thursday. We had to get our own drinks, get our own breakfast, and we had to keep our room tidy. When we were staying at Grandma's we had this big drawer and we had to put all our clothes in it, and our books in another drawer, and dirty clothes in another.'

In Addenbrooke's, William and his parents were beginning to adjust to the prospect of lengthy treatment. They had been told on the day that William was admitted that he would be in hospital for about six weeks – perhaps more, perhaps slightly less. When the diagnosis was confirmed, they knew that William would have to have two separate blocks of chemotherapy over a period of weeks.

The pattern of William's days and weeks began to emerge more clearly: tablets to be swallowed several times a day, and mouthwashes to be used regularly to kill infections; daily blood samples to be given for testing; antibiotics to be administered daily by way of the drip, and, to begin with, anti-cancer drugs as well; one series of anti-cancer injections every two days; and a separate set of injections once a week. Every fortnight, a lumbar puncture to be undergone and a bone-marrow sample to be extracted. Whenever analysis of a blood sample showed that the levels of William's red cells or of the blood's clotting agents, the platelets, were falling too far, blood transfusions were necessary. And all the time, as Dr Tizard recorded, William's condition fluctuated.

'William's tummy pains caused us quite a bit of worry over the next few weeks. They seemed to settle down and then got worse again. The treatment for leukaemia affects both normal and malignant cells; and the effect on the gut could cause complications. We had to be very careful and monitor his abdomen with ultrasound.' (Ultrasound scanning is a technique by which high-frequency sound waves are directed at tissues in the body – or at a baby in the womb. Some of the sound waves are absorbed, others reflected, so that a black-and-white picture is built up on a video screen.) 'One of the drugs we use can slow up the gut. That can lead to constipation and can therefore be the cause of pain. But with William's fever continuing, we felt that we had to go on using antibiotics. He was quite unwell over the next few weeks.

'He came into hospital in much better condition than a lot of children. Some have bleeding problems, or they may be unwell with infections. We always say to all parents that we may make their children worse before they get better, not only because they've got leukaemia, but because of the added insult of all these drugs. The drugs may make them feel sick, they may give them mouth-ulcers. They often feel worse for the first couple of weeks – until we've got rid of all the leukaemic cells and the normal cells can start to regenerate.

'Some children sail through it. Some have a very hard time. William certainly worried us with his tummy pain for a while, but he never had any major upsets. I've seen children much sicker. We were concerned because we didn't know what was causing the pain; it could have been some infection, which potentially would be quite serious. In the end, though, the fever and the pain simply subsided.'

For Sue and Tim, the first two or three weeks were a period of panic. As Tim put it when they discussed it later: 'It was maximum panic initially, and then slowly releasing. But when things happened,

Dr Tizard always gave us the bad news and then gave us hope. Right from the beginning – "William's got leukaemia: that's the bad news. The good news is that we can certainly do something for him. Don't give up hope."'

'But,' Sue added, 'she always made Tim and me aware that she couldn't do the impossible. It was always clear what could happen. But there was always hope, and that's the important thing. She also let us see that she didn't know how things were going to go; she didn't know how William was going to respond to the treatment. Some people can't ever get into remission. The leukaemia never disappears. So we just had to wait and see how William responded.'

Sue was worried that William might be upset when chemotherapy caused him to lose his hair. She remembers a boy who had cancer of the bone, 'a very friendly boy of about thirteen. He used to wave to William as he went past in the corridor, and I made a point of talking to him; so William was very accustomed to bald-headed children long before he went bald himself. It was the fashion in Addenbrooke's to have no hair, and William liked to see the different hats that came in.'

For Tim, Addenbrooke's was a world out of time. 'The days were very, very long – and yet incredibly short. Sue and I would get up at six in the morning, and there was nothing to do other than administer what William had to take. We had to put all his food through the microwave, and make sure that everything he drank was sterilized or came out of a sterile container. He drank orange and lemon squash, mostly. He spent a lot of time watching television – he had a video, and we used to watch cartoons. And he had his keyboard.

'But we never got to bed before midnight, and then we'd be up two or three times in the night when he had tablets and things. And the nurses would be in and out all night as well – every half-hour or so, checking the drips, taking his temperature.

'The only break we had was when we went to the hospital shop to buy some food, or if Sue was there and I went out into the town.'

William always took an interest in what was going on. 'They started giving me injections in the leg. They took blood tests every day from day one. They put special bags on the drip for chemotherapy. They were looking at my blood count. And very slowly it would go down and down, until finally it came up again, so I could come out of isolation. And there was medicine, and tablets, lots of times a day. One was a pink medicine. I really hated it. It was steroids, and later they changed it to tablets. The drugs made me feel dopey, and sick a lot.'

46

Sue and Tim used to be responsible for seeing that William took his mouthwashes and tablets. Sue remembers that Tim bought William a set of miniature darts, and made him a little dart-board out of a cork place-mat. 'He drew the board on it, and William used to throw the darts at it. But as time went on, he didn't have the strength to stand and throw the darts, so he put the cork mat on the floor and just leant over the side of the bed and dropped them. Or he'd just pretend to throw the darts. And when it came to taking his medicine, Tim would play a game with him. He'd say, "You can throw a dart at my nose", and William would pretend to throw. Then Tim would ask, "Did you get my nose? OK, now take your tablet." It was a big game because he could delay having his tablet by however long he took to aim and throw his dart, but he'd take a tablet for every dart he threw.'

William wasn't lonely. He had quite a number of visitors, but they couldn't come into the room. 'There was an intercom, between the door and the window, into the corridor. You'd press a button to listen and speak – you could speak to people who came to see you. But I was in a bed by the outside window, so Mum would normally go and do it. I really just lay there and played – games, and card-games with Dad: I'd hold my cards in the hand with the drip in . . . my arm was very stiff the first time the drip came out. And I had letters from family and friends; I had a lot of letters from the school. And when the holidays started, one or two people wrote from home, or sent cards.'

Nearly every day someone from Tim's family came to see Tim and Sue and to wave through the window at William. Using the intercom, it was difficult to do more than exchange greetings and ask William how he was. Among the most regular visitors were Tim's brother, David, and David's fiancée, Jo. For David, it was important to work out the role he ought to play. 'Believe it or not, my big concern was for Tim and Sue. I felt that William had his Mum and Dad, so he was OK; and it was my job to look after my brother and sister-in-law. But you couldn't help worrying about William. I remember going to the hospital one evening when William wasn't so good. He was just lying there, frail and thin, and I really thought: is he going to be able to pull out of this?'

David's fiancée could never bring herself to face the fact that William might die. She used to collect newspaper cuttings about children who'd had leukaemia and got better, and give them to Sue to encourage her. Sue used to think: that's all very well, they're pronounced cured . . . but that's not William. Jo could see how strained Sue sometimes looked. 'She got very thin. I remember we arrived at the hospital one day, and Sue was very down. William was worse. It was quite late, and Sue was about to phone Tim at home because she had to have a cry with somebody. We picked the right time. She said, "You've saved me phoning Tim. He needn't get it. You can have it instead." So we sat in the parents' room, and Sue said she was convinced there was no hope . . . William had suddenly got so thin, in just a few days.'

Sue's friend, Rosemary Wood, had her own reasons for finding a visit to the hospital an emotional experience. 'The first time I came to see William was the first time I'd made the journey to Addenbrooke's since the day my sister-in-law died. On that day I remember being stuck at the traffic lights and crying and crying, trying to get there before she died. I walked into Addenbrooke's with my sister-in-law's baby and, going into the lift, a woman said, "What a lovely baby!"; and I said, "Yes, and his mother's dying." I re-lived all that as I walked up to see William. And it was awful because, when I got there, William was so ill.'

Many of William's visitors brought something for him. Some presents were an instant success, others were put on one side. It was not that William was ungrateful, but there were times when he lacked the energy to express interest. Rosemary Wood's son, Alexei, brought a BMX Flyer, a battery-operated computer game. Sue remembered its reception: 'William opened the box and, instead of putting it down, all of a sudden there was a spark of life . . . and away he went. He didn't really talk to Alexei, but he played with that game for days. He even used to take it out in the middle of the night, when he was wakened by the nurses.'

There was traffic in the other direction, too. In the ward reception area, Sue noticed a bread-basket full of brightly coloured knitted bees, mounted on gold pins. 'A mother whose child had leukaemia liked knitting; and she had the bright idea of making pretty little bees and selling them to raise money for the ward. She got all her friends to help. They cost 30p each; and I bought one and wore it when I went home. In no time, everybody was busy selling bees so that I could take the money back to Addenbrooke's.'

Mrs Appleby encouraged her son, Jonathan, to take them to his school. 'The High School has six hundred pupils, and within days all the girls were wearing bees as ear-rings. And Jonathan went to the swimming club with his tee-shirt covered in them; the minute the children saw them, they wanted them – and the mums were forking out the money. He made sixty pounds.' Mrs Appleby was very concerned about William, but she did not want to go to see him. In termtime it was difficult for her to visit – 'Plus,' she said, 'I'm a bit of a coward. It would have upset me.'

Mrs Appleby was not the only person to avoid going to Addenbrooke's. Sue knew that some of her family could not face the idea. 'I don't think either my father or my mother could have coped at first with seeing William in hospital. Looking after the other three children was their way of coping and not having to visit. I think my father was afraid of his reaction when he saw William – because sometimes, when you saw William, it choked you.'

'You shouldn't have favourites, should you, but you can't help it,' Neville says; William, being the first grandchild, had always been Neville's favourite. 'Of all the people in the world, it had to be him. You think: Why? But there's no answer to it, really. You've got to accept what is. You can't alter it. If we could have done, we would. Though, if one child out of three thousand gets leukaemia, you'd have a job to pick the right one, wouldn't you? I remember I drilled a field when William was first ill, and afterwards I couldn't remember doing it. It takes about two hours, and I tell you this: I had three goes at it. So I couldn't have done much when I got there, could I? But I didn't want to go visiting. We're not really very good hospital visitors. The first time I went to see William, I was taking Sue back. I hadn't a clue where to go. I hadn't been in Cambridge for fifteen years – the roads weren't there when I first went up. But in our minds we'd pictured William worse, really; looking worse, anyway. He was quite like what he'd always been. We were in the dark, we didn't know anything about chemotherapy and all that. But he wouldn't say much, not through the intercom.'

William's grandmother, Jean, noticed that to begin with Neville didn't even want to talk to William on the telephone: 'When William rang up, Neville sat in the kitchen and said, "I don't want to talk to him ... I don't want to talk to him." Then one day William telephoned and Neville picked it up and answered. After that it was all right.'

The telephone was a lifeline for Sue: 'Tim and I used to phone home two or three times a day. We had a phone in William's room, but it was a pay-phone. William hadn't learnt to reverse the charges at this stage. But Dad would send him money for the telephone, and so would Gran, Tim's mother, and Tim's brother. There was always five pounds in change next to the telephone. William would ring up friends like Alexei, and they'd have man-to-man conversations.'

As the days went by, the routine of hospital began to be matched by the routine in Terrington St John. Sue's parents did not simply transfer the three younger children to their own home; for much of the time they moved in to Sue and Tim's house. One of Sue's sisters came to help for a few days during Easter week. Every morning, once term started again, Jean Poole would give the children their breakfast and take them to school. Then she could go home to attend to her own work before collecting the children, giving them tea and putting them to sleep in their own beds again. As time passed, Sue and Tim found it necessary to leave Addenbrooke's every few days and go home – to keep in touch with the children and the business, and to attend to the necessities of daily living. Then Jean was free to go back to her own house. 'When Susan came home, though,' Jean points out, 'we didn't leave her alone much.'

'Mum and Dad didn't ever leave me,' Sue remembers. 'Tim was left overnight with the children, but I wasn't.'

'Susan came home lots of times,' Jean says, 'but when she came home, she wasn't really here . . . her thoughts were back at the hospital. She might just as well have stopped there. You couldn't get back to the hospital quick enough, could you, really?'

'Well, I'd phone the hospital at eleven at night and there'd be an X-ray machine going into William's room. He'd be having tummy pain again. And I'd panic. I was sure there must be something wrong if it couldn't wait till morning.'

It wasn't only William's abdominal pains that could be worrying. On another occasion it was decided that William's blood count had fallen unacceptably low. As expected, the chemotherapy had affected his blood-making capacity. As a result the supply of platelets, the cells which act as clotting agents and prevent bleeding, was inadequate. The temporary remedy was straightforward – a platelet transfusion, via the drip which was already in position.

Tim was alone with William after the transfusion had begun. 'William suddenly began to shake. His whole body shook. The whole bed shook. He changed colour, went very white; and different parts of his body were hot, and other parts stone cold. They had mentioned that something like this could happen – that the transfusion could cause a reaction – and they just gave him an injection to stop the shaking. He was a bit dozy at the time, so he didn't panic, but it was frightening, the first time I saw it. It was another experience I didn't forget.'

The interest in William's illness was not confined to family and friends, nor even simply to the village. The local press took up the story. To Tim, not used to dealing with journalists, it was a shock.

'We certainly hadn't told the press anything about William getting leukaemia. I think they picked it up from the fact that Mrs Appleby was trying to organize a sponsored swim. Obviously the idea was to raise as much money as possible for leukaemia research; and someone at the swimming club worked on one of the local papers. The paper rang us up, and they just wanted to know the details. We wanted to encourage these young swimmers to do as well as they possibly could. We realized they were doing it for William. The swimming club members had bought William his keyboard by this time, and we were very grateful for what they'd done and what they were planning to do. So the paper printed a story – and they got it right. But then it was picked up by the other local paper. And they rang Sue.'

Sue remembers the occasion: 'I'd been staying overnight with Mum – this was within the first ten days or a fortnight. I'd said goodbye to the children, and I'd gone home to pick up a few things. I think I'd got twenty minutes before someone was going to take me back to Addenbrooke's. I made myself a cup of coffee and was going to have a few minutes on my own. I opened the paper, and there was William – "Brave Boy". I remember tears rolling down my face . . . suddenly seeing your child's name in the paper, and reading it. I hadn't got to the end of it when the second newspaper rang up. I was so choked that I didn't want to speak to this man anyway. I said, "My husband's at the hospital. You can phone him." I just wanted to get rid of him. He was crowding in on me.'

Tim was annoyed to be telephoned at the hospital: 'I didn't know Sue had given him the number. He said, "I'd like to write a story . . ." He was just talking to me, and obviously I replied. At that stage I was so naive that I didn't realize he would consider that to be an interview. And he wrote his story with "Mr Clayton said . . ." and then quotes. It was on the front page of the paper and it was entirely wrong . . . how this little boy swam for leukaemia research at the Saturday night gala, and couldn't let his team down – that kind of thing. The clear implication was that he knew he was ill, knew that he'd got leukaemia, but he was going to swim for his team anyway, because the last thing he'd do would be to let them down ... and then on Monday, he was in hospital. It wasn't like that at all. But that's the kind of story they wanted in the paper.'

'I think after two or three weeks,' says Sue, 'Tim and I accepted the press. It was just that all of a sudden your life was thrown into a turmoil. You'd got a son who was desperately ill – and you felt the press just wanted the story: "Little boy dying ... only a few days to live" – a real drama, and a photo of your child on the front page. That was the last thing you wanted at such a time. It's a whole new world, having a child ill, and then having the press on the telephone ... The idea of going to town and seeing billboards: LOCAL BOY WITH LEUKAEMIA ADMITTED TO ADDENBROOKE'S – that's hard. To walk down the High Street and discover that's how they're selling the newspaper ...'

Tim found his own method of distracting his attention from the anxieties and irritations of hospital life. He used to sit and sketch, and a member of the hospital staff, seeing him at work, asked him if he would finish a painting another parent had started. Because he didn't want to leave William, Tim asked if he could paint on the wall of William's room.

'Right opposite his bed I painted Bugs Bunny and Elmer. All I did was to freeze-frame the TV cartoon and ask William, "Which picture do you want?" Then I did a little sketch on a pad, roughed it out, and then laid it out on a grid and transferred it on to the wall. I did a mountainous, wooded landscape with Road Runner; and then a little character sitting on a tree stump. Somebody sent a postcard – I think it was by Arthur Rackham – and I did a little thing from that, too.'

As the days went by, it was still impossible for Sue and Tim to be sure that the treatment was going according to plan, and that William would eventually be cured. They were constantly aware of the fact that with chemotherapy, even if it was accompanied by radiation treatment, there was still the risk of relapse. William could be in remission from the leukaemia for a year, or two years, or five years; but he could relapse, and then he might need another block of chemotherapy.

Gradually, however, another possibility emerged. Sue remembers when it was first mentioned. 'In the first few days Jane Tizard called us into her room and said that William would have to have chemotherapy, and described the treatment. After that, she said, she couldn't be sure, but there was always the possibility of a bone-marrow transplant. We didn't really know what a bone-marrow transplant was, but that's all she said, as if she was just telling us what could be in store.'

To Tim, it appeared that a bone-marrow transplant was being suggested as a back-up if William had a relapse: 'If there was a donor with a suitable tissue type to match William's, it would be possible to have a bone-marrow transplant. From quite an early stage, we were told all the immediate family would have to be tissue-typed to see if a transplant would be possible. But that might not be this year, it might be later. We were encouraged to think favourably of a bone-marrow transplant, even though we didn't know if there was going to be a matching donor. It wasn't emphasized, but it seemed a transplant would give a better chance of success than the standard course of chemotherapy.'

But first William had to be got into remission. Unless that could be achieved, there would be no point in even trying to find out whether there was a possible donor for a bone-marrow transplant. Slowly, as the days of treatment turned into weeks, William's condition began to improve. His fever subsided, his stomach pains and constipation eased. He was less sick. He was very weak, and it was difficult to persuade him even to move from his bed by the outside window to the bed near the corridor window and the intercom; but gradually, as the leukaemia cells began to be eliminated, the blood count of regenerated healthy cells began to improve.

Almost three weeks after William was first admitted to Addenbrooke's, Sue and Tim were told they could expect to take him home within the next seven days for a short break in the treatment. The very next day, however, after the daily blood test, the door of William's room was thrown open. Dr Tizard walked in followed by her colleagues, and told Sue: 'You're free to go.'

To Sue, it was like being let out of prison. 'Suddenly we could do what we wanted, go where we liked. William was even more amazed.'

'When I first went in,' William adds, 'I thought I was in for about six weeks. Then the doctors suddenly ripped the label saying "ISOLA-TION" off the door, and said I could go home. That was a complete surprise – I can remember the TV programme I was watching: Airwolf.'

Sue remembers that it took William about an hour to get ready to come out of his room. He was very weak. 'I told him to go for a little walk . . . he'd never really seen the hospital, and he was allowed to mix with other people for the first time. I said, "Go and say hello to Sheila.

She's only just round the corner." He could barely shuffle along; and when he got there, he couldn't stand up.

'We were so unprepared. It took us all afternoon just to pack. We were stuffing things in plastic bin-liners – we had so much we filled our van and the boot of brother Michael's Shogun. We got off finally about seven o'clock, three weeks after we'd first arrived, almost to the minute.'

CHAPTER 7

Sue has vivid memories of William's homecoming.

'He didn't look well. He didn't walk upstairs . . . he crawled on his hands and knees. That's how weak he was. Even though his blood count was coming up, he looked very ill to me. His hair was beginning to fall out. If you looked at his navy-blue jacket, it was covered in hairs. And later, when he went up to school, into the playground, the other children just picked the hair off with their fingers – off his head, too. The hair just came out. It was like monkeys grooming one another.

'But to begin with, William couldn't cope with seeing anyone. He wasn't well enough, and there was always the risk of infection. So we'd arranged for the other three children to move in with Grandma for the first few days.

'William was so thin. If you'd sat him down in the middle of all the starving children in the world, he would have fitted in with them – after three weeks! He was unbelievably thin. It wasn't Addenbrooke's procedure to put feeds in the drip; but I had the feeling it wasn't lack of food that had made him lose weight so quickly. I thought it might be the cancer eating him away. This was because I'd seen Tim's father go from a big man to nothing . . . all of a sudden the cancer had taken hold. And when he died, his legs – he'd had terrifically solid legs all his life – I shall never forget his legs when he died. And I had visions that this was what was happening to William. When he got home, he was so lifeless. He had no energy . . . he just looked as if he couldn't be bothered. And he had tremendous bruising on the back of his hand where the drip had gone into his vein.'

William was very conscious of his lack of strength.

'In a way I was getting back to walking, just like a child . . . like a baby. I couldn't stand up for more than two minutes . . . sit down on the floor for five minutes . . . get a breather . . . try another two, then sit down again. I was pleased when I could walk from one side of the room to the other. I felt fairly OK, but even when I could get about, if I tried to play games I was more plodding than running. But with steroids [they are one of the standard anti-leukaemia drugs], which I was on all the times, I didn't feel sick; and Mum was pleased my appetite was good.'

Sue watched his progress intently. 'William looked very old-mannish when he walked, bent forward from the hips. But he picked up every day. And he only had one thing on his mind – eating. When he was up and about, we took him to McDonald's, because he wasn't in isolation any more. And it was a question not of six pieces of chicken, but nine pieces. He began putting weight on as quickly as he'd lost it. But I was aware that people looking at him realized he was a very sick child.

'We had a lovely week at home. When he was first ill, I never imagined he would come home again. Within the week he was an entirely different child – you could really see it, great strides each day. Everyone was so pleased. On the third day, the three younger children came home; and on the fourth day, Grandad took William to the sports shop and bought him a full-scale dart-board – and he threw in some new trainers as well. So when he went back into hospital, he went in in good spirits. He was bolstered up to cope with the next session. Of course, William knew what to expect. He didn't worry about it. He knew what he wanted to take with him, and what he was going to try to do when he got there.'

Eight days after leaving Addenbrooke's Hospital, William was re-admitted. Dr Tizard's first concern was to find out whether it was going to be possible to give William a bone-marrow transplant. For most people, the idea of a transplant of any kind is still strange and frightening. It is one thing to read that kidney transplants are commonplace; that eye surgery involving living tissue from accident victims is an everyday procedure; that even heart-and-lung transplants are regularly successful. It was quite another matter to face the imminent prospect of a transplant for William. Dr Tizard wanted to make it plain that a bone-marrow transplant should not be thought of only as a last resort.

'At the moment a bone-marrow transplant is part of the standard treatment for leukaemic children with very high white-cell counts. If they have a brother or sister who's got a compatible bone-marrow, then at the end of the first two blocks of treatment they go straight on to a bone-marrow transplant. If they haven't got a compatible donor, the alternative is a further block of intensive treatment.

'So our first job, when William came back for his second course of chemotherapy, was to find out if he had a matching donor. We couldn't do that earlier, because it would be impossible to match a donor's cells with William's unless we had William's cells to look at as well. When his healthy bone-marrow cells were very low, as a result of the leukaemia and of the treatment, there was nothing for the haematologists to analyse. We had to wait for the white cells to return after his first block of chemotherapy, when he'd been at home for a week.

'We got all the family together at once, to make it easier for the lab. We tested Sue and Tim as well as the three younger children. But parents are only half compatible with a child. A parent can never match completely, because each parent supplies only half a child's genetic material. The other half comes from the other parent. If you are given cells that don't match, your body rejects them. So bone-marrow transplants from parents are much less successful.

'What's wanted is for the donor's cells and the recipient's cells to mix without fighting. The better match they are, the better the chance the recipient won't reject the donor's cells. It doesn't matter whether they both have red hair, or even whether they both belong to the same blood group. What matters is whether the donor and the recipient match at particular points on a particular chromosome within their genetic material. The crucial areas on this chromosome are the areas which determine the body's reaction to alien cells . . . what the body rejects and what it doesn't.

'With identical twins, you can get a perfect match. If you try and match complete strangers, as people do through computerized bone-marrow panels, the chances of a good match are very small – there are so many millions of combinations of the different elements. With non-identical brothers and sisters, you can have a match, though not perhaps a perfect match, provided they have both inherited the same crucial genetic material from their parents.'

Sue didn't pretend to understand the details of the tests: 'At that stage it was all a bit of a mystery to us. But there was no doubt about having the tests done. We all had them at the same time in the clinic, but by different doctors. I had to be very good and brave when I had my blood sample taken, because Harriet was with me.'

With some pride, Harriet adds: 'I watched Mum and I didn't cry a bit. They put a butterfly needle on the inside of my elbow and sucked some blood through a tube, and then through this wide thing with a pole leading to a great big bottle. It wasn't painful.'

Naomi was on her own. 'I was sick. Edward was with Dad. He was screaming his head off. He had to have four nurses and Mum and Dad to hold him down.'

Edward admits he did not behave well: 'Yes . . . I didn't want the needle in.'

'He grabbed it,' says Naomi, 'and pulled it out and ran towards the door.'

'I tried to run like that man on the TV.'

Meanwhile, William began his second, intensive course of chemotherapy, given over a period of five days. Once again Sue and Tim could not help worrying, but William, although still in isolation, was not as ill as he had been during the first course. He did not lose any more weight.

Tim, who spent most of the week at home with the younger children, felt that he had seen it all happen before. 'We'd seen him go down before and come up again . . . so although you couldn't be prepared for the unexpected exactly, you just accepted it. We were aware that there could be setbacks without it necessarily meaning disaster. It was made clear that William's condition would fluctuate.'

William found it easier, too. He knew what injections he would have, he knew the doctors, and he knew that afterwards he could be isolated, if necessary, in his own home. He was also encouraged to think that a bone-marrow transplant would be possible. 'The doctors said it shouldn't be too hard to get a donor. I had a brother and two sisters and a Mum and a Dad . . . somewhere in that lot there was bound to be a compatible donor.'

The doctors were putting a brave face on it. Mathematically, every child has one chance in four of matching a brother or sister. With two sisters and a brother, William had three such one-in-four chances. But the mathematics of probability are complicated. Having three siblings did not mean that William had three chances in four of finding a match. Theoretically he had thirty-seven chances in sixty-four, a little under fifty-eight per cent. If he'd had four brothers and sisters, he would not have had a hundred per cent chance, but only a little over sixty-eight per cent. In fact, however many brothers and sisters he had had, there would never have been any absolute guarantee of a match. In situations like his it is impossible to reach one hundred per cent certainty.

At the end of a week, William was ready to go home again. It was a Sunday, and Tim's brother, David, arrived to help Sue pack up. Tim had been at home, and was to collect Sue and William in the car.

While away from the hospital, with his dealer's eye always open, Tim had managed to do a little business. 'I'd been to an antiques fair at Bury St Edmunds the previous Wednesday, and I'd bought six very dilapidated long-case clocks – grandfather clocks – from a chum of mine, and a nice little carriage clock. I took two to the shop, and left four in Auntie Pearl's garage in Cambridge. So there we were, with William and me and Sue in the Volvo and four of the clocks as well.'

Sue found it amusing. To pick up a sick child from hospital with four grandfather clocks on the roof-rack seemed a curious reminder that everyday life had to continue.

As a result of the second course of chemotherapy, William's blood count was still falling when he was discharged. So this time, once home, he could not mix with outsiders for fear of infection: His only visitors were his grandparents. However, it was less of a struggle for him to take up normal activities than it had been the time before.

'The second time I felt a lot better,' William says. 'I was still on steroids and eating well. I was slowly getting there. I was finding walking easier. Every few days I could go for half a minute longer, but I couldn't ride a bicycle. I spent the days sitting around, watching TV, playing with our old computer and with the new games people had brought me.'

While William was at home, he had to go to the local hospital at King's Lynn every other day to have his blood tested, to make sure his blood count had not fallen to a dangerously low level. On the third visit, nearly a week after the end of the treatment, the figures for the blood's clotting agent had reached a worrying level. He had to be re-admitted to Addenbrooke's, and then, to add to his disappointment, he started to run a temperature and his stay in hospital was again extended.

Dr Tizard didn't seem very surprised. 'Most children who have this intensive treatment come in at some stage after it's finished. William came in because his platelets were very low, and in that case there's a risk of bleeding spontaneously. You can in fact manage with a much lower level than the normal and still be relatively safe; but below a certain level, we keep children in. If there are signs of bleeding, we give them extra platelets by transfusion. But platelets given by transfusion don't last very long, so there's not a lot of point in giving them unless there are actual signs of bleeding. William didn't have any.'

William was stoical. He felt bored, but at least he did not have a drip. However, when he showed signs of becoming unwell, Dr Tizard was concerned. 'We were just about to send him home again – he had a slight temperature, but he'd been doing very well and his platelet count had started to come up, and that suggested that the bone-marrow was recovering. At that stage, problems are unusual; but that afternoon William developed a high temperature, and we didn't think we could risk it – he looked as if he might need some antibiotics. We were being rather careful because of the problems he had had with his tummy at the beginning. We treated William, even though we never found any positive evidence of an infection.'

The laboratories at Addenbrooke's took a fortnight to analyse the blood samples taken from William's potential transplant donors. Waiting for the results, Sue and Tim had mixed feelings. The idea of a transplant was alarming, yet medical opinion seemed to favour it. On the other hand, extended chemotherapy already appeared to be producing good results. Was it necessary, let alone desirable, to change course? One thing was certain: like Tim, Sue wanted William to have the opportunity of a transplant, even if he might not need to take advantage of it.

When the news finally came, it was better than Sue could have hoped. 'For me, it was rather like being told you're pregnant – but in this case I was having twins, because there were two possible donors. Both Edward and Harriet matched William.' The corollary of that was that if it had been Naomi, and not William, who had developed leukaemia, there would have been no matching donor.

Dr Tizard received charts recording the areas on the crucial chromosomes where there were matches and mismatches. Both Harriet and Edward matched William equally well. But evidence emerged concerning William which Dr Tizard had not expected. She explained its implications: 'The lab had been looking at the chromosomes of some of William's leukaemic cells. Sometimes you can get an abnormality in such cells which is usually found in a slightly different leukaemia from the type William had. But, of course, such things can happen in any type of leukaemia. No one really knows whether they have any significance. It was just another indication that we should be going for a more aggressive treatment – for a transplant. And because we don't do transplants at Addenbrooke's, the next stage was to find somewhere where we could fit William in.'

When Sue gave William the news, he, too, had no doubt about what should be done. 'I thought: If that's what's going to make me better, I might as well do it.'

To many laymen, the mere word 'transplant' is frightening; but that was not how it sounded to Tim's family, as his brother Michael recalls: 'It was a bright light on the horizon. Before that, the feeling had been very subdued. And though we'd tried to be hopeful, we'd heard things that weren't very bright at all. So there was new hope – which was something Sue and Tim got from the doctors; and Ann did too, in a way.' One of Ann's colleagues, a Sister in the ward in which Ann worked, knew a child who had had a transplant six years before, and was well. That, too, confirmed a general feeling of hopefulness.

Sue's parents were not so sure. They knew nothing about bone-marrow transplants, and they were not alone in believing instinctively that a transplant was a desperate remedy.

When William's family doctor, Ken Doran, heard that a transplant was being arranged, he was surprised. '"Risky" was my initial reaction. Was this heroic medicine? Were they simply saying, "We must do something"? And then I thought: It's a long time since I've been in hospital; things change so rapidly these days – even reading the journals, it's hard to keep up. They know more than I do. Go along with it and see what happens.

'From the beginning I knew they'd get William in remission . . . I would have been surprised if they hadn't done that. But when I was talking to Tim initially, I wondered how long it would last. Because what they do know is that once you come out of remission and the leukaemia returns, it's ten times more difficult to get back into remission again.'

Once the decision had been taken in principle that William should be referred to a hospital with facilities for transplants, Dr Tizard began searching for a place for him. It was a process that might take some time.

After all the discussion of his case, William by this time knew more about leukaemia than most lay people. 'I was told to think of a big factory being taken over. Leukaemia cells are coming in and they're getting into the main parts of the factory . . . and they're making the white cells grow more than they should – they suddenly get bigger. And I was told about the different cells: haemoglobin and things give you colour . . . platelets protect you . . . the white-cell count keeps you from getting illnesses and things, and attacks them as well. And I found out quite a bit from some books I got. I was given one by a friend: *Tell Me Why* – a thousand questions, with answers on the same page. And in this book there was "What is Leukaemia?", so I found out.'

While William was under observation because of his low platelet count and his high temperature, Tim was trying to keep the business going. He used to leave the hospital for much of the day, buying and selling, visiting antiques fairs or arranging to be represented by Ann's husband, Mick, who was also a dealer. In the shop Tim's helper, Claire Shewring, had to manage without him.

'I didn't feel under any terrible pressure,' she says, 'I thought I could cope. Tim's assistant in the workshop, David, also rose to the occasion. He was very helpful and would give estimates to customers for the cost of jewellery repairs. The customers were very, very patient. I simply explained that Tim was away because his son was in hospital, and I don't think we lost any customers at all.

'We get very few casual customers, passers-by . . . a few tourists in the summer. Mainly our customers are people who've built up a relationship with Tim because he's a craftsman and a very outgoing person; people do come back because of Tim. Although I organize the shop, I think it's essential that customers have as much access to Tim as possible. Of course, the beginning of the year had been traumatic as well, when Tim's father was very ill, and died. Tim was out of the shop a fair bit then. We had a little bit of a rehearsal for William.'

Tim's main preoccupation was always with William, not the shop.

'I won't say I never thought about business when William was ill, but I never worried about it at all. I realized I was very fortunate in having Claire and David to rely on. And I never had any problem about buying stock. People would bring things into the shop and leave them. I'd have a look at them when I came in, and leave a note with Claire of how much to pay for them.

'But when I was sitting next to William and he was asleep, I didn't think about the shop . . . I switched off from business entirely. I didn't think about money in the way that I'd thought of it before. The overdraft didn't matter. The mortgage didn't matter. Nothing was as important as fighting what we'd got to fight. And I knew if, at the end of the day, the business folded because I hadn't been devoting enough time to it, there would be enough reserve in the value of the house to clear the overdraft, clear my debts . . . and I'd start again – in a caravan in the corner of a field if necessary. Money didn't mean anything at all.'

Once William's deficiency in platelets had been made up and his blood count generally had begun to improve, he was no longer kept in isolation. His temperature was still high, but falling day by day. One afternoon William's grandparents arrived to visit him and were allowed into his room. Neville Poole and William played a game of darts on the new dart-board his grandparents had bought for him. Jean had brought a tin of red salmon which William ate in sandwiches.

The following Monday, after Sue had spent the weekend at home, her parents drove her back to Addenbrooke's and visited William again. The idea of William's leukaemia was gradually becoming more familiar and less terrible.

'We came and sat in his room,' Neville recalls, 'and a little girl came and crept in, a little elf. She was really nervous. She brought her chair and sat against me, and we all watched the cartoons. William thought she was lovely. She was only a toddler. She had a diet problem, and quite often she lived on the ward.'

Meanwhile, Sue went to look for Tim, who had been painting another mural in the parents'· room. She found him by the reception desk in the middle of the ward. Sheila, the ward clerk, said hello and asked if Sue had had a good weekend. Sue, thinking about her question, realized what a strain such brief visits home imposed.

'I said, "It's definitely easier being here with William than being at home." I had gone from a very sick child to three lively ones who were being slightly spoilt. They'd all be crying, and I'd think: How do I sort this out? I mustn't get cross with them the minute I walk in.

'There was also the fact that I didn't know what William was doing, what was happening to him . . . I had to cope with that . . . and Mum and Dad. I was very aware that I had to talk to them and tell them everything. I'd come back from my weekend break absolutely exhausted, and to some extent, as time went on, I was quite pleased to get back.'

But there was to be no let-up. Sue found that Tim had news. 'He told me that the whole family had to be at the Royal Free Hospital in London at nine o'clock on Wednesday morning for a consultation and tests – this is Monday afternoon, 2.30, when I got the news – William would have his transplant on 2 June, and he would have to be in hospital by 27 May to get ready for it. So that suddenly made it only two or three weeks away, when I'd been thinking in terms of three months.'

And there was another complication: the BBC wanted to make a film about William's transplant.

CHAPTER 8

Addenbrooke's Hospital in Cambridge had a close working relationship with the Hospital for Sick Children in Great Ormond Street in London. It was natural to expect that since Addenbrooke's Hospital did not have facilities for bone-marrow transplants, William would be given his transplant at Great Ormond Street. Unfortunately, there was no vacancy in the Great Ormond Street transplant programme until September, more than three months away. At the end of so long a period, there would be an increasing possibility that William's leukaemia might have returned before the transplant could be given; so other transplant centres were contacted. Unexpectedly, the Royal Free Hospital was able to offer William a place at the beginning of June – hence Tim's surprise announcement to Sue that the whole family must present themselves in London in two days' time.

The news that the BBC wanted to make a film about William was an even greater surprise. For some time, staff on the BBC's documentary series '40 Minutes' had been considering the idea of following the progress of a young leukaemia patient undergoing a bone-marrow transplant. The producer assigned to the project, Julia McLaren, spent some weeks talking to doctors who specialized in the treatment of childhood leukaemia and visiting transplant centres round Britain.

The project needed careful planning. The right patient had to be found, undergoing a bone-marrow transplant in a hospital willing to allow all the related procedures to be filmed. The patient had to be suffering from a type of leukaemia that gave a transplant a fair chance of success. Ideally he, or she, should be old enough to understand what was happening and to take an active part in the programme; he would need an equable temperament. Above all, perhaps, the patient, and the family, must be sympathetic and articulate enough to strike a chord in the hearts of viewers.

The Royal Free Hospital at Hampstead, in north London, was one of the hospitals Julia McLaren had visited. Her proposal had been welcomed in principle, but, as elsewhere, no obvious candidate for filming was in sight. Then William's name was brought forward to fill the unexpected vacancy in the transplant programme. The suggestion that he might be the subject of the film was discussed with Julia McLaren and passed on to Tim at Addenbrooke's.

'Dr Tizard came to me while I was painting in the parents' room and gave me the news,' Tim recalls. 'William's transplant was going to be on 2 June and we'd got to go and see Dr Brenner at the Royal Free on Wednesday. And there was a possibility that the BBC might want to film us. She just said, "Well, it might help you through it." She was encouraging . . . but not pushy. She gave me Julia's number to phone. I phoned Julia up about six, and she explained basically what she thought she wanted to do, and the general idea of the programme. She made the point that most viewers have no idea what a transplant involves, and that it would be worth while to let them see the whole thing from beginning to end. I told her that I would ask William, but I said that I didn't think I would want to do it, and nor would Sue.'

Sue agreed: 'My immediate reaction was that we just couldn't do it. It was something we couldn't do and didn't want to do. Then we discussed it with Jane Tizard, and she didn't pressurize us either way.'

Tim was still unenthusiastic when he talked to William about the idea, but William was ready to think about it.

'First of all Dad said, "It's going to bring publicity. I'm not sure that's what we want." And I was thinking about it, and I suddenly thought: well, if it's going to help other people, let's do it! And I started to get excited about it, I suppose. It *was* a little bit exciting – thinking of seeing myself on the screen.'

'William's immediate reaction, I mean before I'd talked it over with anybody outside, was: "It might help somebody else," ' says Tim. 'But really it was very naive of me – asking a nine-year-old boy, "Do you want to be on telly?" Because by this time he was in quite good spirits anyway. So I got back to Julia on the phone that night. She said that if we agreed to be filmed on Wednesday at the preliminary consultation with Dr Brenner, and then we decided we couldn't cope with it after all, then we could stop. I thought: right, if the BBC are prepared to do that (because I realized that it was an expensive thing to do a day's filming), if they're prepared to risk having that thrown away, then their approach is going to be a sympathetic one. They'll be understanding about it all.

'Once Julia said "Yes" to that, I told her that I was almost certain we could agree to the whole filming project. But we'd just have to see how it went on Wednesday . . . I realized in my own mind that if in the end I didn't want to be filmed, we could have made it so awkward for the crew that it would be stopped – not that I'm the sort of person who would do that deliberately, but if I felt it was getting intrusive, then I could put my foot down hard enough to keep the crew at bay. But it was Julia's professional attitude that encouraged us to go ahead in the first place.'

The sudden decision to send William and his family to the Royal Free Hospital meant urgent changes in Sue's domestic arrangements. It was decided that Edward, Harriet and Naomi would spend the night at Addenbrooke's before the journey to London, so that they could all make an early start.

Unlike Sue, Tim always likes to allow plenty of time to reach appointments. 'We left Addenbrooke's at seven. But the exit we normally used was locked, so I had to find another way out, collect the car, and bring it round to the emergency exit by the playroom. Then we had to get all our kit in – what a panic!

'We headed towards London, on the road to Royston. I went down the A10, which isn't a particularly good route – I'd never been down it before . . . I'd always used the A1; and I didn't recognize the roundabout at Royston where I should have turned off. I went straight on down the A10, the traffic was unbelievable, and there were roadworks on the dual carriageway leading to the North Circular. We were only just in time.'

The Royal Free Hospital is a complex of modern tower-blocks standing on a steep hill not far from the lower end of Hampstead Heath. The area round it is one of London's more desirable and expensive inner suburbs, though with less architectural charm than Hampstead itself, half a mile further up the slope.

Tim and Sue were to see Dr Malcolm Brenner, senior lecturer and consultant in the hospital's Department of Haematology. Then William, Harriet and Edward were to give blood samples to establish more precisely how good the match was between William and the other two. Naomi had simply come for the ride, so that she could get to know where William was going to be if he did have a bone-marrow transplant. Sue and Tim felt that it was important that she shouldn't be excluded.

But so far no final decision had been taken about whether or not William was to have a transplant. Today's meeting was to give them a better idea of the pros and cons in William's case. But as they already knew, the principle of a bone-marrow transplant is fairly simple, and the arguments in favour of it are persuasive.

One of the reasons why it is difficult to be certain of curing leukaemia by conventional methods is that the means used to destroy the cancerous cells also tend to destroy the healthy immature cells in the bone-marrow – and some of these immature cells must survive if a supply of mature cells to the blood and the immune system is to be restored and maintained. Both drugs and radiation are indiscriminate in their effects: they destroy cancerous and normal cells alike. So, although cancerous cells are more vulnerable than normal cells to both drug and radiation treatment, it is impossible to make sure that all the cancer cells have been eliminated without risking fatal damage to the normal cells in the patient's bone-marrow.

If a leukaemia patient has a matching donor, willing and able to provide a bone-marrow transplant, this difficulty is partly overcome. The doses of drugs and radiation used to kill cancerous cells can be greatly increased. The patient's own bone-marrow will be destroyed in the process, but it will be replaced by healthy and compatible bone-marrow from the donor. Thus the chances of completely eliminating the leukaemia are much improved, and the inevitable threat to the patient's supply of cells to the blood and immune system is sidestepped.

But there is a second advantage in a bone-marrow transplant, which is that the incoming marrow also targets itself against the leukaemia. If any leukaemic cells are still left at the end of chemotherapy and radiation treatment, the incoming bone-marrow recognizes the leukaemia as foreign and starts attacking it. So there is a double benefit in a transplant.

At his first consultation with Sue and Tim, Dr Brenner was not chiefly concerned with scientific and medical explanations. He wanted to give them enough information to allow them to decide for themselves whether it was right to submit William to the risks of transplantation or not.

Before the interview started, the '40 Minutes' film crew arrived to set up their gear: a cameraman and his assistant, a sound recordist, and Julia McLaren to direct operations. The camera tripod was only seven or eight feet away from its subjects, but although at first sight it seemed as threatening as a one-eyed triffid, experience told her that it would soon become virtually invisible, as would those members of the crew who remained in the room, motionless and silent, while the consultation was recorded. When everything was ready, Dr Brenner took his place, with a colleague next to him. Tim and Sue were asked to come in. They shook hands and sat down. There was no formality, but no chat.

In general, Dr Brenner shared the optimism expressed at Addenbrooke's about the treatment of leukaemia, but with reservations. 'For a child with leukaemia, the treatment has improved a lot over the last ten years. The groups with the best prognosis can get very high cure rates just by chemotherapy – around eighty per cent, or even more. But the group with the best prospects is very tightly circumscribed. They would be girls, and under the age of ten or twelve. Initially they have to have a very low count of white cells, malignant cells, because that's an indication of the extent of the disease; and they also mustn't have any growth abnormalities within those cells, because abnormalities make the cells much more resistant to conventional treatment.

'Now, William had scored badly on all those points. He was male, he had a high white-cell count when he was admitted to hospital, and he had particular chromosome abnormalities that we know, from following up trials of drugs in patients, are predictably associated with a poor response to chemotherapy.

'What I wanted to do with Sue and Tim was to talk to them about the overall advantages of a bone-marrow transplant, but also to make them aware of the problems and the risks. And I wanted to know whether they realized that it was possible William had already been cured – by the chemotherapy he'd already had.'

To begin with, Tim acted as spokesman: 'I said that what Sue and I understood was that, with such a high white-cell count at the beginning, the chances of William relapsing were likely to be high. But at Addenbrooke's they hadn't put a figure on it.'

Dr Brenner believed it was important to provide some figures. 'I told Tim and Sue that with the kind of leukaemia William had, his chance of being cured by chemotherapy – and with a nine-year-old like William, the chance of being completely cured is the only thing that matters – was around twenty per cent; and that he had an eighty per cent chance of relapsing. And although, when he'd relapsed, another treatment could get him into remission, that remission could be short-lived, and his chances of cure then would be very small.'

The figures were not what Sue had expected. 'They were quite a shock for us. Tim and I had never been told that William had only got a twenty per cent chance of a cure, if he didn't have a transplant.'

On the other hand, Dr Brenner explained that if William did have a bone-marrow transplant, then his chances of cure went up. They would go up to about seventy per cent. But they wouldn't go to a hundred per cent. 'The chances are not a hundred per cent because, despite the high doses of chemotherapy and radiation which a bone-marrow transplant allows, and which can wipe out much more leukaemia than ordinary treatment – despite all that, he still had a twenty per cent chance of relapsing after the transplant had been accepted.

'And what made the decision much more difficult was that he had a ten per cent chance of dying from a complication of the transplant itself. I thought it was very important that Sue and Tim should realize that.'

Tim was shocked. 'I didn't realize that the risk of dying from the transplant was as high as that. I knew there was a risk, but not as high and dramatic as Malcolm made it at the interview.'

'I made it clear,' Dr Brenner says, 'that not all the risks from the transplant were immediate risks. Some of the risks come from infection, some from the rejection of the graft; or the graft could itself reject William and attack him. We could do things to minimize those risks, but statistically we still had to say that ten per cent of children will die from the transplant. So what Tim and Sue had to consider was that there was a twenty per cent chance that William had been cured already, and that they were going into a procedure which might kill him. That sounded bleak, but the point was that in all probability he would survive and be cured.'

Sue raised another possibility. What would happen if they let William go on as he was, but, if he relapsed, then go for a transplant? Dr Brenner agreed that it was certainly possible to do that. 'But what happens then is that the chances of cure by the bone-marrow transplant become very low. After relapse, they're only about twenty per cent. And the chance of cure by ordinary chemotherapy once you've relapsed are virtually zero. So you're back down to the low levels you started with. But some people would do that.'

But there was still the risk that William might not survive the transplant in any case. If he rejected the graft, was that fatal?

'Rejecting the graft is included in the overall ten per cent risk of dying from the transplant. But what we're doing now is saving the patient's own marrow. So we could save William's marrow and keep it frozen; and if he did reject the grafted marrow, we could give him his own marrow back. So we'd be back to square one, as it were, and he would be no worse off than he was when we started.'

If the transplant went wrong with one donor, could they try again with the other?

'That's possible; but I had to tell them that we prefer not to use the second donor, because in our experience – and I think the experience of most other people – if you keep trying to transplant, patients suffer a lot of toxic effects and they have a very high mortality rate from the treatment to get the marrow to take ... so we feel that if it doesn't take the first time, that's really it; we should then give the old marrow back.

'I think people often don't have it made clear to them what a transplant involves. Though overall there's no question that it's of benefit, for an individual person, you have to decide yourself.

'Tim and Sue had never discussed figures before. In a way they're misleading, but in another way they give you something to hold on to. Sue and Tim hadn't realized that without a transplant William's chances were so low. But with the high count of the particular leukaemia he had, I thought it would be very difficult to eradicate without a transplant. He didn't have the worst type of leukaemia, but he didn't have the best.

'You have to leave no doubt in people's minds. It would be completely immoral to do it any other way. You're offering a procedure which overall has benefits, but which for an individual may be adverse. You may kill them needlessly – that's what it comes down to in the end. And then you have to be sure you're getting informed consent to whatever is going to be done ... that everyone knows what's going to happen and what the prospects are.

'Sometimes it's very difficult to get through to people. I know that people often complain that doctors don't tell them anything. The reason often is that doctors *don't* tell them anything. But the reason can also be that the patient's level of anxiety is so high they just cut off – they don't take in what the doctor says. I could see that Tim and Sue were both absorbing it.

'In general we do try to have at least two of us talking to patients, so that there is less of a communication problem. If the person conducting the interview misses something out, or says something confusing, the other one can pick it up. But also the person conducting the interview may not appear on the wards very much ... he might be away or in the lab. So it was good for Tim and Sue to be familiar with at least one person from the first interview, so that everyone knows what's going on.

'I had Dr Robbins with me, as the witness, the silent witness. And that can be important if there is a misunderstanding later and a distraught patient says, "You never told me." It has happened once. It wasn't a parent, it was a wife. It was terrible for everyone. Sometimes a transplant does go wrong, particularly with adults at a very advanced stage of disease, where there really is no hope through conventional treatment. A transplant is the only possibility, but they've already been exposed to a lot of damaging drugs, and the body's in a weakened state ... a high proportion of those end in fatality. But at the end of it, if people can at least feel that everything possible was done and everybody did their best, you can go away, not happy, but at least not too disturbed. But if people feel you misled them and robbed them of three months with a partner or a child, that's devastating.'

As the interview with Tim and Sue went on, more details emerged. Dr Brenner broke down the ten per cent risk that the transplant itself might kill William. The risk of his rejecting the grafted bone-marrow was about five per cent; the risk that the graft might attack him was perhaps one per cent; the risk of infection while William's own defences were in a weakened state amounted to about four per cent.

On the other hand, the twenty per cent risk of relapse after the transplant might be an exaggeration where the patient was a child. And it was encouraging that William had not been exposed to prolonged chemotherapy and was able to have a transplant without delay now that he was in full remission. Even so, Dr Brenner warned Tim and Sue against rushing any decision.

'I told them they must think about it. They mustn't make a decision that day. And I said again how wrong it would be for me to say, "Yes, it's great ... this is the cure."'

Sue's first impression was that Malcolm Brenner was cold-blooded: 'When Tim and I walked in and he said there was a ten per cent risk that the transplant might kill William, it was quite a shock. We'd only left Addenbrooke's that morning with "Goodbye, good luck", and they'd been so excited at having two donors and the Royal Free taking William so quickly ... But Malcolm went on to point out what the transplant might do for him, and, of course, my hopes started to build up again.'

So did Tim's: 'Quite simply, it was a question of looking at the mathematics of it, an equation ... which side was going to weigh heaviest in William's favour . . . and that's what we did. To go from a twenty per cent chance of avoiding relapse to an eighty per cent chance, you've got to risk that first ten per cent chance of dying from the transplant, haven't you?'

Originally both Sue and Tim felt inclined to leave a transplant as a last resort. But they were forced to reject the idea. As Tim saw it, there was no point in doing that, for two reasons: (a) you were going to have to get him into remission a second time, which is more difficult; and (b) he would have had a certain amount of treatment already, so you wouldn't have been able to give him as high a dose as you really needed for the transplant'.

Sue was also aware that William was in good spirits. 'He'd only been ill for two months. What would it have been like if he'd relapsed after two years, and he'd been backwards and forwards for treatment? It would have been the last straw – "Two years doing all this and it's still not done." He hadn't been in hospital long enough to feel fed up.'

In the end, Tim's view was clear. 'A transplant was a battle rather than a prolonged war. And the odds – well, seventy to thirty for you is better than twenty to eighty against you. I approved of the way Malcolm handled it. Some people might not want to know how bad it could be, but for me personally, the first thing I want to know is the worst possible outlook. From there on you've got nothing but hope.'

Sue, too was grateful for Dr Benner's clear exposition of the possible benefits, and the risks. 'Malcolm brought us back to reality. We knew exactly where we stood. We'd been galloping away, galloping down the transplant road, and he made us realize that we'd still got a lot more bends to negotiate. But we came away feeling fairly happy about it all. We were going to go ahead with the transplant.'

Whether that decision would have been as clear-cut, or whether it would even have been the same, had Sue and Tim known that in Addenbrooke's Dr Tizard put William's chances of survival without a transplant at fifty per cent or more, no one will ever know for sure.

CHAPTER 9

After Sue and Tim had finished their consultation with Malcolm Brenner, William was called in to join them.

'What I told William first,' says Dr Brenner, 'was that a transplant would make him better more quickly than the other treatment. He wouldn't have to be in hospital for lots of different courses. He'd have this one treatment and then it would be finished. He would have to visit us occasionally afterwards, but he wouldn't ever have to stay in for a long time.'

There followed a long and complicated recital of the transplant procedure. The day-to-day timetable was spelt out and the different stages of the treatment explained. It was made clear that William was going to have several operations, that he would again be given drugs that would make him sick, that he would be in isolation. The shortest stay he could expect in the Royal Free would be four or five weeks. William said little, but, being already familiar with some of the procedures, gave the impression of taking a good deal in.

Meanwhile, the other children were being looked after by the hospital staff in the corridor. From time to time they poked their heads round the door of the consulting-room. They made friends with the members of the film crew who were outside, and Edward demanded to be shown how the equipment worked. Among the outpatients waiting to be seen at the clinic along the passage, there was a sudden interest in the family that was going to be filmed.

When Dr Brenner had finished with William, all the children except Naomi had blood samples taken. These were needed for more detailed tissue-typing, which would decide whether Harriet or Edward would make the better transplant donor. This time Harriet was not quite so calm. She felt sick, and went white. Edward screamed loudly again, and had to be held down.

In humans, chromosomes occur in pairs, twenty-three pairs in all. One of these pairs governs (among many other things) tissue compatibility. When a child is born, he or she inherits one chromosome of this pair from the father, one from the mother. If two children inherit the same tissue-compatibility chromosome from their father, and also inherit the same tissue-compatibility chromosome from their mother, then they will be identical at the major tissue-typing sites in their genetic material. They will have the same mechanisms for identifying and rejecting alien tissue. Their own tissues will therefore be compatible with each other. They will match.

Harriet, Edward and William had all been established as identical at one major tissue-compatibility site on the relevant chromosome. The odds therefore were that they would be identical at the other major tissue-compatibility sites, since they were located on the same chromosome. But sometimes there is a phenomenon called 'crossing over', where one bit of a chromosome hooks on to another chromosome and they exchange information, so that although people appear to be identical – to have inherited exactly similar chromosomes – in fact they are not. Tests on the remainder of the relevant chromosome had to be carried out by the Royal Free Hospital's laboratories.

When all the blood samples had been taken, the whole family and the film crew went up to look round the ward where William would stay if he had a transplant. Then, after a cup of coffee in the canteen with the crew, and more formal mutual introductions, Sue gathered the children for the long drive home.

The first thing they wanted to do was to call at a Happy Eater café. The journey was long and tiring, but the family stopped at Addenbrooke's to deliver the news, and to give an official letter to Dr Tizard. To Sue, the return to Addenbrooke's seemed like going home.

Once back in their own house, the family resumed normal life. William, though he had been discharged from Addenbrooke's, still had to follow a strict regime of medication. In the twelve days left before he was due at the Royal Free, he visited Addenbrooke's for a blood test only once. He even went back to school. His movements were slow, and he couldn't walk far; he found running very difficult. Otherwise he behaved and looked like a normal child, though – to Sue's regret – his hair was very wispy.

No formal decision was ever taken about whether William should have a transplant. For Sue there was no need.

'When we left Malcolm Brenner, Tim and I had no doubt that William was going to have one. We were supposed to phone Malcolm up to say yes or no, but we never did.'

Tim explains: 'We didn't say no, and Addenbrooke's told the Royal Free that we wanted to go ahead. I signed a form later to say that if

74

experimentation was required – for William to take part in antibiotics trials – that would be quite all right, and another form before William went to theatre. William's own reaction was that if a transplant was part of the treatment and it was going to make him better, so what? Get on and do it. He never questioned it.

As for Sue, 'there were two things about that day at the Royal Free, and there was no question of "Shall we or shan't we?" about either – the transplant or the filming. We found we didn't mind the filming. We didn't come away and discuss it; we just knew from the start that it was all right.'

A week after the consultation with Malcolm Brenner, Julia McLaren and the film crew went to Norfolk to spend a few days recording the Clayton family's activities. It was at this point that Sue first met the co-author of this book – myself, Nicholas Woolley. I was Julia McLaren's reporter. The idea of the '40 Minutes' documentary was to record what happened to William and his immediate family during his transplant. The main interest was in the people concerned, not in the scientific aspects or medical techniques; but enough of the science was to be explained to make it clear to viewers exactly what was happening. Normally it is not the style of '40 Minutes' to use a reporter. In most films shown in the series there is very little commentary, and what there is is written by the producer. During interviews, the producer asks the questions. When the film is put together, the questions are mostly cut out. Those that are left remain as the product of a disembodied voice.

But in this case, the editor of the series decided that the technical information needed by the viewer was so important that it would be wise to use a reporter, albeit a non-specialist, to sift and present it. That would leave the producer free to concentrate on the content and style of the pictures. Such a decision adds to the cost of the filming, but it sometimes improves the quality of the result. Certainly, in my experience over many years of making both long and short films, it is useful (as well as reassuring) to have two minds to consider what should be filmed and how the filming should be done. Besides, I had been a colleague and friend of Julia's for a number of years at the BBC. To join her in a major project would be fun.

It sounded a straightforward exercise, but for the film-makers and the family there were potential difficulties. The most obvious was that the process of filming might impose too much strain on William or his family. It might expose him to unnecessary risks. Or it might get in the way of the doctors and nurses, and have to be abandoned. In practice, goodwill, careful planning, tact and perseverance can nearly always avoid or get round problems. The number of projects aborted for such reasons is small.

The worst fear was that the transplant might fail: William might die as a result of it, or the leukaemia might return later. If that happened, what should be done? For the programme-makers and the BBC it would be wasteful and frustrating to throw away all the film they had shot. Yet it would be misleading and irresponsible to devote a whole programme to a failed bone-marrow transplant, when the figures showed that most succeeded. For the family, to watch a television programme record William's progress towards death might be a bitter addition to the anguish of bereavement. Or would such a programme be a memento to be cherished, and a worthwhile memorial to a courageous and uncomplaining child? It was a dilemma that had to be discussed. Julia McLaren and I told Tim and Sue that we could not promise not to use the film we shot if William died; we had to retain control of the material (as the BBC always insists, as a matter of principle); and that the most likely outcome would be that we should use some of William's story in conjunction with other material which would give a more balanced view of bone-marrow transplant as a treatment. Where that material might come from and how it could be combined with William's case history to make a satisfactory programme, we had, at that time, little idea.

Tim had long faced the idea that William might die: 'You're aware of it, but you convince yourself that it's the last possible thing. You put it out of your thoughts because you've got a battle to fight, and you can't fight if you're worrying about it.'

Sue was doubtful whether she had really come to terms with it. 'I don't know whether you can, until it happens. It's something you put to the back of your mind. You just keep going while you can . . . while William's happy. We had to carry on, with the doctors doing their best.'

On that understanding, briefly agreed and never written down, Tim and Sue allowed the filming to go ahead. It was a sign of great trust which Julia, the film crew and I tried not to abuse.

It is worth adding that Tim and Sue were not offered any substantial financial inducement. In the normal course of events the BBC would pay a small fee to the main contributors, but in this case the money was given to leukaemia research.

*

The period between William's discharge from Addenbrooke's and his admission to the Royal Free Hospital was a time of readjustment for the whole family. The three youngest children had to get used to William again. Naomi in particular, as the oldest of those left at home, had to come to terms with the realities of William's situation.

'I only got to visit William once in Cambridge,' she recalled later. 'In the beginning I didn't know anything – until Mummy came home and told us William had leukaemia, and he would have to have a transplant or the anaesthetic or something. She seemed worried – because she knew William might die. I didn't. Mum didn't tell us till about six weeks later . . . 'cos she thought, "I won't worry them yet, until they've got over the fright of William being in hospital."

'At Grandma and Grandad's it was just normal. They knew William could die, but we didn't. They never told us they were worried about it. They were specially nice to us, but we weren't really spoilt – because we had to sort of do the jobs; and we didn't get any pocket money because we had sweets. Sometimes we were naughty, but we had to behave quite well or we got told off.

'Then, before the transplant, we knew it could be serious. William would go away to hospital, and he could die.'

A few days after the family's visit to the Royal Free Hospital, news came of the blood tests which would decide whether Harriet or Edward was to be the donor. Edward, then four, recalls nothing of that time. Harriet claimed afterwards. But then she went on, rather blurred recollections, partly coloured by hindsight but partly reflecting the mixed emotions of the time.

'Out of all the family I didn't specially want to be the donor,' Harriet claimed afterwards. But then she went on, 'One day Mum went to get the result of the blood tests . . . and when she got home, she said it was Edward, but she was teasing. It was me. I was happy . . . but then I got a bit rude. I suppose it was very important to have the transplant, or William would die. If he had a donor, he would perhaps live. I thought it was very important.'

William remembered that time more clearly. 'Harriet was quite pleased when it turned out to be her. At first we thought she was going to make a face and say, "I'm not going to do it." She had been acting a bit like that after they'd taken the blood tests at the Royal Free. But she was OK. She seemed to be fairly pleased.'

Sue's interpretation of Harriet's reaction was based on maternal scepticism. 'We knew we would have had trouble if Harriet hadn't been the donor. She was the only one who had never had the excitement of going into hospital. She couldn't wait to get the results, and I expected her to cry if Edward had been chosen. I thought the fear of the unknown would make her cry anyway. But she said, "Yippee ... great!", dancing round the room and telling everyone. Then an hour later she'd gone all quiet. And she became quite demanding, as if she knew she had something which we all wanted.'

In the end, the reason Harriet was chosen was not that she was a better match than Edward: there was nothing to choose between them. But she was older and bigger. She could understand better what was happening, and should suffer less physical and mental stress.

There was another theoretical advantage in choosing a female donor. Female cells are always distinguishable from male cells. Therefore if the transplanted bone-marrow were to be female, and male cells appeared in William after the transplant, they would be instantly recognizable as survivors from his own bone-marrow. Such identification would be convenient, but not particularly important. It would not necessarily be a sign of relapse. It would simply indicate that not all of William's marrow had been eliminated. That is not uncommon. About a year after transplant, very small numbers of lymphoid cells (cells of the immune system) and myeloid cells (blood cells) begin, as it were, to creep out of the woodwork.

The disadvantage of using a female donor with a male recipient is that the transplant is more likely to attack the recipient's own tissue. As a boy, William carried a Y-chromosome, the chromosome which determines maleness. On the Y-chromosome there is a tissue-compatibility antigen which transplanted female cells can recognize and react to. There is thus an increased risk of what is called 'graft versus host' disease (GVH).

There was one thing that could be done to make Harriet a better donor. Dr Brenner asked Dr Doran to give her the standard vaccinations against diseases such as hepatitis and tetanus. She would then be able to pass on her immunity to William.

It takes time for the different members of a film crew to become a coherent team, and to get to know their subjects. Though Julia McLaren and I were used to working together, neither of us had worked more than briefly with any of the four other members of the team. Nor were the camera crew who joined us in Norfolk the same as the crew who had filmed at the Royal Free Hospital. For our own benefit, but even more for the sake of the family and the hospital, Julia had made special efforts to ensure that from this point onwards a single crew would film the rest of William's story, but there was no absolute guarantee that the overlapping schedules of various projects would allow it. On this occasion we had the luxury of meeting at lunch-time over sandwiches in our hotel in King's Lynn, while Julia outlined the project and the likely filming schedule.

As in many documentary films, there was an initial problem to be solved. In one sense we were breaking into a story that was, perhaps, half-way through. We had to explain who William was, and what had already happened to him, before we could move on to the transplant itself and film at least the main events as they happened. We had to introduce Sue and Tim, and the three younger children. We had to give some idea of how the family lived; and we had to find some means of telling, and perhaps illustrating, the story so far.

The first stop after lunch was at Tim's shop. A shot of the exterior would give a fleeting glimpse of the locality. The window display could show some of Tim's jewellery, and the kind of antiques he liked to buy and sell. But Julia needed Tim himself. What more natural than that he should take a piece from the display while the camera filmed from outside?

One thing which usually strikes outsiders about the process of filming is its artificiality. Tim frequently needed to take things out of his shop window, but film-makers, even the makers of factual documentaries, do not wait upon the event if they do not need to. They create it. For this shot the window display was changed to include what Julia felt was a more representative, or perhaps simply more visually interesting, collection of objects. Tim was instructed to wait for the appropriate moment before performing his action. From across the road, the camera panned down the outside of the building, and the signal was given so that Tim bent over into the window just as the shot reached him. There is plenty of scope for error. The timing may be wrong. A car may pass between the camera and the shop-front. Tim may glance at the camera. The cameraman may decide that he was shooting too wide, or too close. When everyone is satisfied, the action is likely to be repeated, so that a close-up of Tim leaning into the window can be cut into the edited version of the action. In fact several different angles might be tried.

Then the crew moved inside the shop. Again, to create the right effect, Tim had to find something to do. He persuaded an old friend and customer, who happened to be visiting, to act as the prospective buyer of a gold repeating pocket-watch. The sound recordist had to find a position where he could hold his microphone near enough to record the conversation without getting into the shot. Once again, to allow the essence of the scene to be transferred to the television screen in a fraction of the time it actually took Tim to demonstrate the watch's mechanism, Julia needed several shots from different angles. By this time the second characteristic of filming was beginning to become obvious: its time-consuming nature. Two simple picture sequences had taken more than an hour.

The film convoy then drove to Tim and Sue's house at Terrington St John. It consisted of three cars: Julia and her production assistant, Jane, were driving a hired car; Chris, the cameraman, and his assistant, and Keith, the sound recordist, used an estate car large enough to carry all the gear; and I travelled in my own car. Sometimes the cavalcade can be even more unmanageable if the production assistant and sound recordist, perhaps starting from different bases, each travel separately. On many projects there would also be an electrician, with a separate van. '40 Minutes' films, however, for economy and convenience as well as for stylistic reasons, normally do not use portable lights.

It is not surprising that one of the commonest misfortunes endured by film-makers is to lose a vehicle from the convoy – and to realize only then that the missing member of the team does not have the address of the next location. It may take an hour or two before contact is re-established by telephone messages relayed through the film operations manager in London.

Film-makers sometimes forget that, to the people being filmed, the crew can appear like an occupying army. The house is filled with strangers, humping in camera, tripod and recording equipment, together with what seem to be dozens of large boxes. The furniture is moved to make a better background for interviews. Someone seems perpetually to be on the telephone, making long-distance calls. The dog gets trodden on and has to be turned out into the garden. Time is forgotten and the convenience of the subjects ignored. Yet such is people's good nature that before any business is begun, tea and coffee are being offered to the invaders, sandwiches are being cut, sometimes whole meals prepared – and often by people who might well have better things to do with their time and money. So prevalent is hospitality that film-makers sometimes abuse it, asking, as they walk through the front door, 'Is the kettle on then, dear?'

Having taken the decision to allow a film to be made of William's bone-marrow transplant, Sue and Tim seemed ready to take the consequences. They accepted the paradoxical need to re-order events and re-arrange the surroundings in order to present a picture on the screen that gave an accurate impression of real life.

In one sense Sue was grateful to be told what to do. 'I was quite pleased that Julia could come in and go round the house and take this photo and that photo to put on top of the piano. That was quite nice. I didn't have to think . . . there was no point getting anything ready for Julia because she knew where she wanted to go and what she wanted to do.'

Tim, too, discounted the artificiality. 'With a very basic knowledge of cameras it was obvious why everything was being done; so you just get on and do what's best for the film crew. You can't say, "No, I don't want to be filmed in that chair there, I want to be filmed sitting here." But I was surprised at how close the camera was when we were interviewed. In fact the interviews were the hardest thing of all, because we didn't know quite what questions were likely to be asked. We'd thought about the questions . . . but we hadn't found answers.'

As a reporter, I found both Sue and Tim willing and sympathetic interviewees. This was not, of course, the first time I had met them. Because Julia and I had travelled up to Norfolk to see them a few days before, I was familiar with William's story in outline. I had not mastered the details, nor had I unravelled the complexities of their family relationships. But in many ways that was an advantage. It is easier to ask questions in a straightforward way, and evoke straightforward answers, if the questioner does not know too precisely what the answers are likely to be. If he has too little background information he may waste time and irritate his subjects by making false assumptions, but too much preliminary discussion, in an attempt to get to know one another, can be inhibiting. Feeling that they have already told the story once, the interviewees find that they cannot reproduce their original spontaneity.

Sue and Tim described vividly William's diagnosis and treatment so far. They spoke with self-possession, lucidly and apparently without reservation. I was impressed by Sue's willingness to examine her own feelings.

'Nick asked me what William's illness had done to me,' Sue remembers, 'but everything had happened so quickly, I hadn't had time to consider. I knew it had changed my attitude to life . . . and to the children. I didn't need to worry how the children looked, or what the house looked like, or things like that. There are more important things in life: enjoy every day as it comes; make the most of every day . . . you don't know what's round the corner any more. Of course, you didn't know before, but leukaemia makes you realize what can happen to you.'

I also interviewed William. To an outsider, as I was then, it was extraordinary to think of William as a boy possibly under sentence of death. He was pale, and his white-blond hair was almost gone, but otherwise there was nothing to distinguish him from any other healthy nine-year-old. He certainly did not appear to be frightened by the prospect of the treatment to come, as Sue confirmed: 'He never let us know that he was frightened. Just occasionally, at bedtime, he would ask a question that made me realize that he was thinking about it . . . but I don't think he was frightened.'

Talking to children, especially sub-teenage children, and getting them to respond, takes a special knack. It is important to treat them as equals and not to talk down to them, but just as important not to talk over their heads. Julia set up the camera in William's bedroom. He sat on his pine bed, with a photograph of Liverpool football team on the wall above him. Toys and games lay piled on the desk and the table next to it, and a dozen rosettes won in horse shows and riding competitions hung on the wall opposite. I asked William about the things he enjoyed doing – at home and at school. His answers were factual, to the point, and readily given, but – to begin with at least – they mostly consisted of a single sentence or even a single word. Gradually, as he relaxed, they became longer. He told the story of his illness so far, and explained what was in store for him at the Royal Free Hospital. He described his physical state. He said he was looking forward to being at home again for his tenth birthday at the end of July. But he said very little about his feelings. In the course of the interview I asked him what the doctors at Addenbrooke's had said was wrong with him. He answered, 'Leukaemia.' He did not mention the word 'cancer', although he knew that leukaemia was a form of cancer. I did not ask him whether he knew that he might die, although I knew that he did. On balance, I think the decision not to put that question explicitly was right; but it is difficult to draw the line between legitimate inquiry, designed to reveal the subject's character and state of mind, and unjustified and distressing intrusion. At the end of the interview I had the feeling that I had not done a very good job.

That evening, we filmed William swimming with his club in King's

Lynn. Next day we arranged to film in school. It was the last day before half-term, and the vicar, Mr Wright, was coming in to take assembly. Sue took the children to school and stayed to watch. She had warned William that he was likely to be given a present.

After the service, the headmaster explained that William was going into hospital in London and would not be back in school until after Christmas; so they had decided to give him a radio cassette recorder, a ghetto-blaster, on which he could play tapes of news sent by the school, and send recorded messages back. The presentation was made by the vicar. William, self-possessed and polite as ever, came out from his desk to accept the present and say thank-you. Afterwards the children crowded round to look.

'Lucky boy, William,' said one child.

'How do you get leukaemia?' asked another.

Sue wasn't surprised that the school had expressed their good wishes in a tangible way. At least, 'I wasn't surprised they had a collection, but I was surprised that the PTA also added some money. I think they had about sixty pounds. That's a lot of money. I found the filming of assembly hard. I watched from the door into the next room – and I cried. I wondered if I would ever see my four children at school together again. Every word of the hymn seemed to mean something special. They were all singing about autumn leaves, and I couldn't help wondering what would be happening in the autumn.'

William did not stay for the whole day at school. In the afternoon Tim drove him to London, to the Royal Free Hospital.

CHAPTER 10

They went straight to the radiotherapy department. William was to be measured and tested, so that when the time came he could be given the correct dose of radiation in preparation for his transplant. The consultant radiotherapist was Dr Teresa Tate.

'Radiotherapy before a transplant has two main purposes,' she explains. 'One is to kill off any leukaemic cells remaining after chemotherapy . . . after drug treatment. The other is to suppress the patient's immune system so that he will tolerate the graft, the marrow which is coming from someone else and so is not native to the patient. The third possibility is that you actually have to kill cells in the patient's bone-marrow to make space for the new cells when they come and settle down. When the donor's marrow is infused into the patient, the new cells home in to the patient's bone-marrow cavities and start to grow. If there's no space for them, they don't grow as well. But that's more theory than established fact.

'If you look at the first purpose of radiotherapy before a transplant as the killing of leukaemic cells in the bone-marrow, you find that if you prime a patient only with drugs, you quite often get a recurrence of the patient's own cells some years later. They're not necessarily malignant, but they do show that you haven't obliterated all the recipient's cells, and you may have run a greater chance of the leukaemia recurring. If you use radiation as well as drugs, and you test the patient's bone-marrow afterwards, you will generally find only donor cells. Without radiation, the risk is that you might leave one malignant cell – and in theory one malignant cell is enough for the cancer to re-grow.

'Whether the cancer does re-grow depends on the malignant cell's capacity to go on dividing – malignant cells have a greater capacity to do that. Probably everyone at some time develops some sort of a cluster of cells growing in an out-of-control way, but the body's immune surveillance system spots it and stops it. Certainly the body seems to have some power to attack malignant cells. People develop cancers only when the surveillance system fails.

'There is another benefit from using radiation to eliminate leukaemic cells. Radiation sterilizes areas which are not satisfactorily treated by chemotherapy ... areas which drugs can't reach – principally the central nervous system and the testes.

'The second main purpose of radiotherapy before a transplant is to suppress the recipient's immune system so that he won't reject the donor's bone-marrow ... not to obliterate it, but to suppress it, so that it can't spring into action when the patient is given the marrow. I say that because, in practice, there is always a possibility that the patient may reject the graft; and I think that shows that the patient's immune system has not been totally obliterated.

'The difficulty is that in the past, when we increased the radiation dose and removed more of the patient's immune cells [so that the patient would be less likely to reject the graft], a different danger was increased. It appeared that "graft versus host" disease [the graft reject-ing the patient] got worse. So it looks as if there is some sort of balance between the two risks – between the risk of the patient rejecting the graft and of the graft rejecting the patient – so that you probably do need some sort of residual immune response in the recipient to keep "graft versus host" disease down.'

William was stripped and positioned in a small bucket-seat at right angles to the beam of radiation from the X-ray machine. His knees were drawn up and his hands clasped round them. A total of twenty-six small test discs were attached to each side of his head, shoulders, trunk and legs, to measure the radiation at each point. Round his body were packed bolus bags, like bean bags, filled with a silicon material which has the property of absorbing radiation at the same rate as human tissue. By administering a very small dose of radiation and measuring how much was absorbed by the test discs, Dr Tate could calculate how much radiation would be needed to produce a full dose appropriate to William's size. She could also make sure that every part of his body would get an equal dose of radiation.

'We have to be very careful about the dose we give,' she says. 'Obviously, children are broadest at the shoulders; but then they've got lungs, which contain a lot of air and absorb radiation less than solid tissue. And then you come down to the ankles, which will absorb proportionately more, if you give enough to produce a good dose at the shoulders. The point of the test was to measure William up and find a position in which the dose would be as even as it could possibly be. If you like, we were building him up with the bolus bags to be the same width at his ankles as he was at the broadest part of his body. And we used his chest X-ray to work out how much lung-volume there was in his chest, compared with other tissue.'

For total body irradiation (TBI), the X-ray machine can be operated at anything from four million to eighteen million volts. The X-ray beam originates from a thin sheet of tungsten less than a centimetre across, and spreads out in the shape of a cone, with more or less the same energy right across it from edge to edge, at any one point.

'William had to be hunched up in the little chair so that we could get the whole of him into the beam. Obviously the beam goes on getting wider and wider, the further you get from the point of origin; and if we had a longer room we could actually treat a patient lying down. But as we've only got four metres to the wall, we have to squash them up. It's OK for someone William's size, but if you're a six-foot-three man, it's difficult.

'When working out the dose, it's the lungs we prescribe for. They are what we're most concerned about. The X-ray beam produces millions and millions of pulses of energy which pass through every cell in the body – any one cell may be hit two or three times. All tissue that reproduces itself rapidly is affected – the gastro-intestinal tract, the lungs, and, most of all, the cells in the bone-marrow, including the cells of the immune system. They are the most sensitive. So we have to achieve a dose that will kill the bone-marrow cells but produce a very low level of damage to the lungs.

'What radiation does is to stop a cell's ability to reproduce. So the cells where the damage is most pronounced and shows up most rapidly are the cells that reproduce themselves most quickly. Other cells are less badly damaged and the damage shows up less quickly. But it does seem it's only if the nucleus of a cell is damaged, and even certain substructures within the nucleus, that the cell is killed. If the pulse of radiation going through doesn't hit the critical part of the cell, the damage will be repairable; and after a short time – a matter of hours – the cell is back to its normal function.

'To calculate William's dose, we took measurements from the test discs on both sides of his body. One hundred per cent of the radiation will hit his right shoulder, say, and thirty per cent will come out of the left shoulder on the other side. You need to know that, so that the dose can be evened up when he's turned round half-way through – you'll give the hundred per cent to his left shoulder and add it to the thirty per cent he's already had. With the energy of our beam, you can get a good dose just by treating him from one side and then the other.

Some people find that with a lower energy beam, they have to treat from the back and front as well as from the sides.

'You can't get an immediate reading from the test discs. The technique of using them is called T L D – thermoluminescent dosimetry – because they contain small packets of lithium fluoride, which has the characteristic, after radiation, of giving off illumination when you heat it. You put the discs in a little oven and bake them for about twenty-four hours; then you can measure the pulses of light they give off – using a mechanical reader – and that tells you how much radiation has been absorbed. Over the next few days, we were able to do the calculations of the dose William would need when he came for his total body irradiation as part of the transplant procedure.'

For William, it had been a tedious expedition: 'Seven hours away from home for an hour's work!'

It had been even more frustrating for Tim, with nothing to do but watch. 'Half an hour to set William up, and then five minutes' radiotherapy. The highlight of the day was getting batteries for William's radio cassette recorder. The number of garages we had to call at to get batteries! And then all he wanted to do was to listen to police messages.'

Next day, at home once again, William went to play with his friend Alexei, Rosemary Wood's son. She recalls: 'The thing I remember is the children sitting in the chair together, snuggled up watching something on television – quite peaceful, and Alexei looking after William. I didn't think William was really back to normal. He didn't have much hair – he had his cap on a lot. And I know William's always pale, but he looked almost transparent. Then he said, "Can I spend the night?" I felt it was a great responsibility. And of course I phoned Sue up.'

In a way, Sue wanted to keep William to herself, and she remembers her feelings on that evening.

'I can remember being – I won't say unwilling – but being aware of letting him stay away for the night and trusting someone else to give him his medicine and his tablets. He needed sterile knives and forks, too – I was always responsible for pouring boiling water over them, and suddenly I was letting someone else do it. Though, to be honest, all the way along you could have trusted William with his tablets – he was quite capable of knowing just when he had to take them . . . and I always knew he would take them.

'He came back the next morning. He had to be back to go to church, because the BBC were filming there. He came home at ten, and he was fine. And then suddenly a bad headache came on, and you could see he didn't feel very well. I thought: Ah, late nights. Perhaps he shouldn't have stayed with Alexei; he's done too much – all the usual things. I don't think he wanted to go to church . . . in fact I wondered if it was right to take him. He was sick, but he knew the filming was going on, so he got ready. He was pale, and quiet; but the headache went, and by the afternoon he was all right, playing football while they were filming at his godfather's.

'With William, I never worried about overstrain. He never did any more than he wanted to. And when he stayed away from home . . . it gave me so much pleasure to see him wanting to do something, and being able to do it – being with Alexei as he used to before he was ill.'

That evening William went riding. It was something he did frequently before he was ill, and something Julia and I thought would illustrate his wide interest in outdoor activities, if it wouldn't overtax his strength. William was keen, or at least keen to be helpful. Sue made special arrangements for him to have a riding lesson on his own at a convenient distance from Terrington St John. William got dressed in jodhpurs, boots and hard hat. The crew set up in a pleasant paddock surrounded by trees and hedgerows. The pony was led out.

After two or three months' break, William wanted to take things steadily. Julia began to film him checking the girth and stirrups, and getting into the saddle. Once he was mounted, the instructress told him to walk the pony in a circle. William kicked the pony's sides. Nothing happened. William tried again. The pony began to graze.

'Pick up his head and take him round in a circle, William.'

William pulled on the reins and gave another kick. The pony moved off, straight ahead.

'Turn him, William.'

The pony continued to move in a straight line.

'William . . . use your legs as well as the reins.'

The pony began to trot.

'Don't forget to rise, William. Now turn him . . . William . . . make him turn.'

The pony began to canter. Suddenly his objective became clear – the half-open gate, and home.

'William . . . pull on the reins, William. Stop him, William . . . stop!'

With a swerve and a bump the pony careered through the gap between the gate and the gate-post, and disappeared from sight. There was a short silence. Then a rush for the gate. The pony was nowhere to be seen. Fifty yards away across an open field, William was walking dejectedly towards the stable.

The riding lesson was abandoned. The film team left for London. Safely at home, as Sue reported later, William cried.

CHAPTER 11

The following day, Monday, was a Bank Holiday. The family were able to spend it by themselves. In the evening, Sue took the three youngest children to her parents' house. Next day would bring an early start for London.

Sue has a very clear recollection of that morning: 'We left about seven . . . we had to be at the Royal Free at ten. I can remember William leaving his room – wondering if he'd ever see it again. To me, he was saying goodbye. You just didn't know what to expect. You didn't know what was going to happen.

'Dad came down to see us off. In those first few weeks, whenever we went to hospital, he always came and said goodbye . . . six o'clock, half past six, whenever we went, he was always there. He said to William, "We'll see you in six or eight weeks", but you knew underneath it all he was wondering. To Mum and Dad the whole idea of a bone-marrow transplant was so strange. And after the chemotherapy, for Dad, if we could get William into remission – even if only for a year or two – that would almost have been enough for him, at that stage.'

William knew that he was certain to be in hospital for several weeks. Accordingly, he took his own amusements with him – toys, Lego, a stereo, a few comics.

At second sight, the Royal Free Hospital was a surprise. William hadn't remembered it as being so large – four tower-blocks, surrounding a central core. 'We were just to the side of one block. We came in from the main lifts, at the sixth floor, and went right down through some double doors to the end of the ward. Turn right and you come past the ward reception. Keep going, and that was my room at the far corner.'

Riddell Ward was a children's ward, though not exclusively devoted to transplants. It occupied most of one floor of a tower-block and was conventionally arranged. Single rooms and areas with several beds were located against the outside walls, while an internal block contained the reception desk, offices, the sluice-room, the kitchen, the parents' sitting-room and visitors' rooms – many without natural light. The most unusual feature of the ward was the school. Along most of the outside wall on William's left as he first entered the ward were two large school-rooms, staffed and managed by the Inner London Education Authority. Only six London hospitals have such a school.

Sue and Tim had been told that William would have a room in the far right-hand corner of the ward as they approached from the door. But they did not know exactly which one. In fact there were two rooms on the corner. They shared a small ante-room, about eight feet by five, where nurses and parents could put on gloves and masks before visiting a patient who was in isolation. The room facing north, which had a distant view over the rooftops towards Hampstead Heath, was already occupied by a boy only a little older than William. Eduardo Cunha, as they later discovered, was just finishing his first course of chemotherapy. He was suffering from a form of myeloid leukaemia (cancer of the blood-forming system) for which there was no possibility of treatment in his own country, Portugal.

William's room faced almost due east and so got the morning sun, while staying cool during the day. The picture-window looked out over the nurses' home and the neighbouring streets. There was space for two beds between the outer and inner windows. Opposite them, by the door, was a sink with a television set in front of it, and in the far corner a door leading to a shower and lavatory. It was smaller than William's room at Addenbrooke's, but that was not what struck Sue first: 'It wasn't what we expected. It wasn't that it was dirty; but it was tacky. The walls had got Sellotape on them and Blu-tack. You know – when you move house, there are somebody else's marks. It wasn't filthy, but it wasn't sterile.'

To Tim, the room was in need of a ritual cleansing. 'I couldn't believe that William was going into that room to have a treatment that would make him susceptible to any infection, and that they could contemplate leaving somebody else's germs in there at all . . . I almost imagined it would have to be fumigated.'

Sue did not want to be ungrateful, but 'we had a feeling that the other people had just left the room and hadn't made the effort to tidy up behind them. But there were cleaning materials, and Tim and I started to clean up from the first day. I wouldn't want to appear to moan about it. But it just wasn't sterile as you imagined it would be – at school, Mrs Appleby was telling the children that William would be in a bubble; that was the kind of idea people had. I think part of the trouble was the fact that we'd left Addenbrooke's. The room at Addenbrooke's had become our home . . . we'd gone through the first barrier-nursing there. Now that William was having a bone-marrow transplant, the room had to be so much more sterile. And it wasn't.'

Tim had another explanation for the apparent difference: 'Sue and I had gone to Addenbrooke's in a state of shock, whereas when we went to the Royal Free we were better informed and more optimistic; we were on a high – so we were able to observe whether the room was clean or dirty, and we had something to compare it with. When we went to Addenbrooke's we were just in a total maze – we found ourselves in a room in the middle of the night, and we were just grateful for it.'

'Yes,' adds Sue, 'we were starting again.'

'You felt a little bit remote through that second door from the ante-room into William's room.'

'You were away from it all, in a corner. Once you were in your room, you couldn't hear anything.'

The shocks of readjustment continued. Sue did not expect to see Dr Brenner immediately William had been admitted, but she was a little disappointed not to catch sight of Sister Jordan, who had shown them round the ward the week before.

Sue found it a peculiar day. 'Tim and I were expecting a visit from sister or one of the junior doctors, but the first person to come in was David Lee, the charge nurse. He seemed quite a character, but we didn't realize he was actually senior to a sister. Then along came Robert Milnes, one of the teachers, and he didn't fit our stereotype of hospital either. I suppose it was because we weren't expecting them. David was in a white coat with ironed lapels, and epaulettes. We'd been used to doctors in dungarees, sitting on a desk swinging their legs, and all of a sudden we'd got this – a stiff, starchy charge nurse who very much made his position felt.'

Tim got off on the wrong foot. 'Quite honestly, I didn't twig that he was in charge. I assumed that Sister Jordan was in charge of the ward. Some guy with "Team Leader" on his coat – you'd think he was in the Scouts.'

Sue was taken aback, too. 'But there he was, so immaculate he put the room to shame. Then I suppose Tim and I started to comment on the room: it wasn't as we imagined it would be. He said, "You can't expect a sterile room." We asked about a telephone. He wasn't very impressed by that idea, either. He said there wasn't going to be much chance of that. But that was his way. He had to lay down all his rules and laws. It was an awkward moment.

'Then, ten minutes later, Robert Milnes turned up and announced himself as the school teacher. He was overflowing with enthusiasm and took William round to the school to have a look at it. William played the piano for him so that he could assess his standard. Then Robert brought the school computer into William's room, and the BBC filmed us having a game.'

It turned out that David Lee knew north Norfolk well, having trained at King's Lynn. He and the Claytons had acquaintances in common. As a specialist in children's nursing, with four years' experience at the Royal Free, he was familiar with the strains imposed by arriving at a London hospital from elsewhere in Britain – or from another part of the world.

'We're very well aware that patients have had treatment before, stayed in hospital before, and formed relationships with nursing and medical colleagues. They grow attached. But it would be wrong for us to try to compete with their own hospital. They've come here for a purpose – to have a bone-marrow transplant – and to get the best nursing skills to see them through it.

'But it is very important to feel part of something, to have a "home" which is comfortable, an area where they feel safe. And whatever they do to make that environment safe, I'm all for – it may be pictures or bringing a duvet cover or pillow from home . . . whatever they do to make somewhere where they can function more or less normally. You can wash and iron to keep things clean – I think I said to Tim on the first day, "We're not creating a sterile field." We couldn't achieve that. We create an environment that's as clean as possible within normal expectations. To say "It's going to be sterile" – we wouldn't be able to keep to that.

'The thing that parents can do, and enjoy doing, is what we've termed "the clean-care regime", like making the bed, cleaning the room, preparing food. They get very involved. My philosophy is to invite the parents into care. It's too easy to disarm parents by taking over, saying, "We're going to do this now or that now; William's going to have a bath now" – we don't work like that here. The overall aim is to make a child's stay in hospital as un-traumatic as possible. Coming into hospital is already a traumatic experience; if they've got to start conforming to our ways, that's going to make it even harder for them, and particularly for the parents and children who don't come from this country – that must be very strange.'

Not long after David Lee had introduced himself, Sue and Tim were visited by a nurse with the routine forms to be filled in – names and addresses; had William had measles? William submitted once again to the tests and measurements regularly required when a patient is admitted. Later in the day Dr Paul Roderick, who was to have day-to-day charge of William, paid a visit. To Sue he seemed a familiar figure: 'We've got a nephew – Paul Roderick was the spitting image of him. They could be brothers. He came in . . . his tie would be round one way, his coat flung over his shoulder . . . I liked him from the start.'

Tim, too, approved. 'He was down to earth . . . our level.'

William stripped and lay on the bed while Dr Roderick examined him: eyes, neck, chest, abdomen; then the knees for nervous reflexes; and finally the balls of his fingers and the soles of his feet, to see if William could recognize the blunt end of a pin from the sharp. Dr Roderick was looking for signs of infection or ill-health in general, residual leukaemia, or damage to the sensory nerves caused by the drugs William had already had. There was nothing to be found.

For William, bedtime came at nine-thirty. Later, Sue joined him for the night, sleeping in the spare bed. Tim had to sleep in one of the visitors' rooms. Like many hospitals, the Royal Free has been increasing the accommodation available to parents in the last few years. Riddell Ward holds twenty-six children, and if necessary each child can have at least one parent sleeping in the hospital. All the single rooms have spare beds (though it is not always appropriate to use them); there are visitors' rooms in the ward's central block and outside the ward area as well. There is even a Z-bed. But the rooms are often internal, and may have to be shared. They do not offer luxury. Tim was sharing with the father of a kidney-transplant patient. He had a bad night.

'To be honest, as long as you've got a bed to be near your child, you don't mind you're sharing a room with someone who speaks a different language. But the noise of the extractor fan was unbelievable. It was really dreadful. They'd got paper in it, which made it worse. And the dust attracted by the fan was all over the ceiling.'

Next day, Wednesday, more sophisticated tests began, to discover whether William's previous drug treatment had damaged any organ or increased any pre-existing weaknesses. The first procedure was to scan his heart and analyse the results on a computer. Radio-isotopes were injected into his blood to make it show up on the scanner. A second injection was given to prevent the radio-isotopes dispersing themselves into the stomach or the thyroid gland. Then William was placed on his back on a table in the scanning-room. Above him the scanner, shaped like a large, flat cheese and about three feet in diameter, was suspended from an adjustable arm. The scanner was swung down until it almost touched William's chest, and angled slightly towards William's left side, so that by turning his head to the right he could see out from underneath it. His right arm hung down over the side of the table.

The nurse explained what was about to happen. She produced a bucket of iced water and asked William to put his hand into it and keep it there for the next three or four minutes. The BBC's camera began turning over. William put his hand into the bucket. Sue watched uneasily. This was a test she had not encountered before.

Ice-cold water gives a shock to the human body and stimulates the heart to work harder. At the same time the cold was constricting the blood vessels in William's hand, and by reflex putting up the blood pressure, thus making it more difficult for the heart to pump blood round the body. It is a fairly crude test to make sure that the heart has not been so damaged by the drugs previously used that normal pre-transplant conditioning would be unsafe. The results appeared in the next-door office on a computer screen which could display a single moving picture of a section of the heart, or on a divided screen showing a number of pictures at once. All would be recorded for later analysis.

At first the iced water was pleasantly cool. 'Think of your summer holidays,' the nurse had told William. But after a minute, the cold and constriction began to hurt. William opened his mouth and shut it again. His eyes began to glisten behind his glasses.

The nurse reassured him. 'I know it's not very nice. You're doing very well.'

William shivered a little. His chin began to tremble. He uttered a little gasp.

'You're doing very well. Try and relax. I know it's easier said than done.'

William was brave. He made no attempt to take his hand out of the water.

Tim looked on, silent but encouraging. 'I can remember deliberately wanting to go away . . . just not to have to be there for a minute or two. I can remember being in the office next door and seeing the pictures come up on the screen while he was being treated. It was good to be in that office, away from what was going on . . . the colours, greens, reds and oranges, the way they sliced through, as if they were looking at a different section of the heart. I could imagine it being sliced, you know?'

The nurse came back to William after checking the computer. 'Still got your hand? I hope so – because I'm not going to sew it back on for you!'

After a couple of minutes Julia stopped the filming. She knew she had quite enough material to give an idea of William's ordeal and his reaction to it. William found it harder to keep his composure once the camera had been turned off. A few tears dropped. Once or twice he cried out, quietly. After a little more than three minutes, he was allowed to take his hand out of the bucket. He was given a minute or two to recover, and then the performance of his heart was recorded as he squeezed a rubber ball.

As was to be expected, neither Paul Roderick nor Malcolm Brenner was present at the ice-bucket test. But Dr Brenner later explained that William was the victim or the beneficiary – it is hard to decide which – of a combination of praiseworthy caution and bureaucratic routine. Some hospitals, for instance the Great Ormond Street Hospital for Sick Children, do not perform the test when transplant patients are admitted.

'They don't do it because almost all their children have lympho-blastic leukaemia [cancer of the lymph cells of the immune system], and it's unusual for the pre-transplant treatment for acute lympho-blastic leukaemic to have ill-effects on the heart – it's also less common in children to get ill-effects anyway: they're stronger, more resilient. So I guess that in William's case we were looking at a low probability. And if, at a place like Great Ormond Street, you put seven hundred children through the test and get only one result, is it worth it? Whereas for us, with more adults, it is necessary. But, of course, we could have said "No" for William, in his first remission.'

This was not the only ice-bucket test that William had to endure. But on later occasions the pain seemed more bearable. This may suggest that anxiety and fear of the unknown are as much a cause of pain as physical suffering.

With Sue as his amanuensis, William recorded the day's events in his diary:

At 10 a.m. I had to go in a wheelchair to Medical Physics for a computerized cardi-scan. I had to squeeze a ball and put my hand in a bucket of ice and water for three minutes. It was very painful. The BBC filmed me. I then went for a chest X-ray, and while we waited for the film I went to Cardiology for an ECG [electrocardiogram] which tests your pulse rate [and records the electrical activity of the heart muscle]. I got back to the ward at 12.30. After lunch the teacher came to tell me about my lessons after the transplant. The BBC came back to film a thorough examination by Dr Roderick, and a blood test. I had tea, watched TV and went to sleep at 7 p.m.

Next day, Thursday, the diary continued:

> I got up early, had a good wash and put on my gown. I had a pre-med at
> 8 a.m., and by the time the porters came at 9.30 to take me to the theatre, I
> felt rather woozy. Mum and Dad came down to the first floor with me, and
> then I saw everyone from the BBC in gowns, masks etc. I can't remember
> much more of the day.

William's bone-marrow transplant did not in itself require an
operating theatre, but it was necessary for him to undergo three procedures in the operating theatre as preliminaries. The first was a
lumbar puncture, carried out in the ante-room to the theatre itself.
The anaesthetist, Dr Simons, a gentle man who had visited William
the night before to tell him what was going to happen, took William's
wrist in his hand.

'Just a little prick, William.'

'Will you tell me when it's coming?'

'Yes . . . a little prick coming now.' And without a pause between
the word and the act, Dr Simons inserted the needle and fastened the
syringe of anaesthetic to it.

'Is this the one that'll send me to sleep?'

'Yes, this is the one. Good boy.'

William's eyes closed, and his head fell to one side.

'Poor little boy,' said a voice. 'He's had a hard time.'

William gave a little groan.

'Happy dreams,' said Dr Simons.

As at Addenbrooke's two months before, a few drops of William's
spinal fluid were drawn from his spinal column through a needle
inserted between two vertebrae. The liquid would be checked to see
that no leukaemic cells had reached William's brain. Then a drug was
injected into the spinal fluid to back up the general chemotherapy
already administered. Under the unrelenting eye of the camera, Paul
Roderick, who performed the two operations, found his hand shaking.

'We were really topping up the cerebro-spinal fluid with drugs to
prevent William from relapsing . . . because one of the sites of relapse
is not only the bone-marrow; you can get isolated relapse in the spinal
fluid. In the old days, when they didn't do all this, a lot of people
relapsed. The cerebro-spinal fluid offered more privileged sites for
leukaemic cells to sit, and the drugs never got to them. So six months
later, having normal blood counts, patients started to get symptoms
suggesting that there was leukaemia growing up again in the spinal

fluid. Lumbar punctures are really a precaution that tends to reduce that problem.'

The second procedure was to harvest some of William's own bone-marrow, so that it could be frozen and stored. There was a one in twenty chance that the bone-marrow transplanted to William from Harriet simply would not take. In that case his own bone-marrow could be put back, and William would at least be no worse off.

For a patient who has no compatible bone-marrow donor, this procedure can be used as a treatment in itself. The patient's bone-marrow is harvested, the leukaemic cells in his body are eliminated by drugs and radiation, and the patient's own marrow is put back. Any residual leukaemia in the bone-marrow is likely to be so diluted that the body may be able to destroy it and allow normal bone-marrow to grow back. The success rate of such treatment is good enough to make it worth trying when no alternative is possible.

William's bone-marrow harvest was performed by Dr Brenner.

'We put William on the table, and with a long hollow needle I made two holes in the skin on his hips at the back – first one side then the other. Pushing the needle through different parts of the bone under the skin, I drew out five or ten mils of marrow at a time until I'd got about a quarter of a litre. (With an adult it would be about half a litre.) The marrow is put into a sterile collecting bag; it goes into the blood processor and the red cells are separated out from it and just the white cells are kept. They contain all the immature, progenitor cells that are capable of growing up into a new marrow. Then they are just frozen and stored in liquid nitrogen. There are no time-limits, but we don't store bone-marrow for years in expectation of relapse – though we could use it for that. We store it really because we hope that after a few years we'll be able to use it experimentally, to improve the techniques of growing marrow cultures for future treatment.

'The US Navy apparently stores bone-marrow for key personnel working in nuclear submarines. In fact, research into bone-marrow transplants was started by the US navy after a nuclear accident in Yugoslavia in the 1950s. They put a lot of money into investigation of harvesting techniques.'

The last procedure was performed by a surgeon. It was designed to prevent the damage which can be caused to the veins of the hand by repeated injections and drips, even if a catheter is left in position permanently.

The surgeon first made a cut low down on the right-hand side of

William's neck and exposed the main vein, an inch or two below the skin, which leads directly to the heart. He then attached a flexible plastic tube, a Hickman catheter, to a long needle, like a sail-maker's needle. This he inserted under the skin of William's chest, six or seven inches from his first incision. He pulled the Hickman catheter up under the skin of the chest until it reached the first incision, detached it from the needle, and inserted it into a small hole made in the exposed vein. With all the tissue replaced, the catheter was held firmly in position, the open end on William's chest taped down and plugged. The effect was to keep the vein clear of any irritation or infection which might be caused by frequent manipulation. The Hickman catheter became the lifeline through which William could be given fluids, food, drugs or blood-products without discomfort.

Sue and Tim, as parents, were excluded from the operating theatre. Julia and I, with the film crew, were privileged spectators. Afterwards we asked Sue and Tim to re-create a minute or two of their long hours of waiting, while we filmed. They sat at a canteen table, silhouetted against a window and discussing (for the second time) the likely timetable of events as predicted by the doctors. Film-makers and subjects were conspiring to present an artificially created moment as reality. It is a necessary technique if a film is to have evocative pictures and variety in pace and mood – but it is dangerous in the hands of the unscrupulous.

Sue and Tim met William in the recovery-room about twelve-thirty. He complained that his neck hurt and that he had a sore throat. As was to be expected, he felt low. His diary, compiled a day or two later, recalled the outstanding events:

> The BBC filmed me back in my room. I slept most of the afternoon, and a drip was attached to my Hickman catheter, and I had lots of fluids to prepare for my chemotherapy. I watched 'Top of the Pops' and Uncle Duffy [Tim's brother, David] visited me. I was sick. I started my mouthwashes.

That evening, eight hours after his operations, William reached the moment of no return in his treatment. With Dr Roderick and a number of others, Dr Brenner came into William's room. The first bag of tissue-destroying drugs was hung on the drip-stand by William's bed and on Dr Brenner's signal connected to his Hickman catheter.

'We gave two drugs, one after the other, in a continuous process. The first was to attack the leukaemia, and to kill as many immature cells of William's immune system and his blood-forming system as possible. The second was to counter the side-effects of the first, which is to cause loss of blood through the bladder.'

This was medication designed to destroy almost all William's natural ability to resist infection. It would leave him without defences against bacteria, viruses, fungi and any other agent of infection. And it would deprive him of the power ever to rebuild his own defences. Sue watched. 'About ten of them came into William's room, some doctors we'd never seen. I was made very aware that there was no turning back. In a few minutes the chemotherapy would begin, and we'd have to go ahead with the transplant. On the other hand, they did reassure us that it was the best chance.'

Tim never doubted that the right choice had been made: 'I was never tempted to say no. I couldn't see there being any alternative. I was more worried about it later than I was then. Later, I had time to think: you were playing with his life. Then, it seemed the only thing you could do, and you did it. It was life-and-death, but I wouldn't allow myself to think of it like that at the time.'

About eight o'clock the tap was turned on.

◆ *PART TWO* ◆

CHAPTER 12

In the corner room next to William's, Eduardo Cunha was recovering from a course of intensive chemotherapy. It was not yet known whether he could have a bone-marrow transplant. With him was his mother, Fernanda. His father, also Eduardo, had recently gone back to Portugal to make the final arrangements to meet the cost of the treatment.

Eduardo could be seen through the glass door of his room, but since he was in isolation, little direct contact was possible. But over the weeks to come, Sue and Tim were to get to know both his parents well. Their experiences en route to the Royal Free Hospital had been even more stressful than Sue and Tim's.

Eduardo was a middle-ranking manager in a large clothing firm in Portugal. He had worked there for twelve years, with responsibility for computer technology. Fernanda had worked for the same company even longer, as a secretary. Their home was in a small town on the coast of Portugal, about fifteen miles north of Oporto. Just across the road from their house was the beach.

About a month after Sue noticed that William was off colour, Fernanda began to worry about little Eduardo. To her eyes, he looked pale, almost yellow. His father was sceptical. So was the doctor she visited. But Fernanda persisted. She took little Eduardo to a second doctor, and then a third, who ordered a blood test. The results were inconclusive, but by the end of April, after a bone-marrow test, a firm diagnosis was made.

Eduardo senior remembers the circumstances vividly. 'I was at home . . . it was lunchtime . . . and someone came and told me to go straight away to the hospital in Oporto. The doctor there said, "I have to tell you the truth. Your son's got leukaemia – myeloid leukaemia. It's the worst kind, and we can't treat it in Portugal. This is really serious . . . we have no cure. Impossible. Probably you must go to Paris or London for a bone-marrow transplant."'

Because he was over ten years old, little Eduardo was admitted to an adult ward in Oporto's main hospital. It took persuasion to get him transferred to a children's ward. There was squabbling among the doctors; and time was short. Little Eduardo's father was overwhelmed.

'We couldn't decide what to do, because we didn't know whether we could get money or not. I was crying. My wife was crying. And the lady paediatrician came and said, "You have to decide if you are going to Paris or London, or where you are going to go, because we need to know whether we should start the treatment here, or not." I felt so angry. I said, "No, I need your opinion. It's not only a decision whether to go to Paris or London. I don't know where to go, with whom to talk, what to do – I don't know anything. And I don't know because I'm not a doctor. If I was a doctor, I wouldn't need your opinion, because I would know the same as you know, or more." "Well," she said, "you'll have to decide where to go." The problem is this: in a certain way, they don't like to send people to Britain. They don't like it because in Portugal they know how to treat leukaemia, and if they agree to send people abroad, everybody thinks that they don't know how to treat it. But they know. Only they do not have the same facilities there.

'I think to send people abroad is one way to fight the bureaucracy – to tell them: "We have to send people abroad because we have not the facilities." And look! It's £80,000 for my son. With £80,000 for my son, and for other children, and adults, they could do lots of treatment in Portugal.

'I don't know how to tell you how it was when the doctor said "leukaemia". The first thing you feel is that you are completely blocked. When I say blocked, I mean to say you can't think, you can't talk, you can't do anything. That's what happened with us. I only started crying, I think, after one hour. But at the beginning it's a shock that stops everything. But then you start thinking that there is no chance. With acute myeloid leukaemia, it could be a few days. It could be three or four weeks, but it's quick. There was a friend of ours in the same factory . . . one day my wife rang me and said: "Fernando's child is in hospital. They said it was leukaemia. Instead of passing urine, he's passing blood." I said, "Oh, this is a renal problem or something. Don't worry." Three days after, he was dead.

'One thing that happened with me . . . I don't want to tell this . . . but one thing that happened: I thought about suicide. I will explain why. I have my son; and my wife didn't want more children because her pregnancy was really bad, and she had lots of problems when he was born, and she was all the time remembering that. So I felt so close to my son that for a long time I could not imagine life without my son. This is not fair, but probably I could live without my wife or without

Above: From left to right: William, Naomi, Harriet and Edward one year before William's illness.

Left: Sue and her mother.

Below: The first mural Tim painted in William's room.

Tim's painting of William
the night the chemotherapy started.

Six o'clock the next morning.

Charge nurse David Lee and Sister Jordan.

A student nurse
playing with William.

Eduardo.

Right: William ready to leave.

Below: William's
belated birthday party.

Above: William swimming in a friend's pool.

Below: William and Harriet relaxing after the swim.

A very special relationship. (David Reed)

Mrs Appleby talking to Edward. (David Reed)

William back in action. (David Reed)

The family.

William now.

my parents or my mother-in-law, but not without my son. He's a special one to me.

'After my Joanna was born, it was different. I adore my Joanna. No one can deny that. But what I felt about my son, I went on feeling. When the doctors said there was no chance, I couldn't imagine life without my son. That is a stupid way to think, probably. I felt it for a few days and then I stopped.

'So in the hospital we asked the opinion of a senior consultant. And I said, "Doctor, if it was your son, what would you do?" And he said, "I would go abroad. And if you want my opinion, I would go to London, because London and Paris, they have nearly the same results. But I still prefer London, because my friend Dr Jimenez worked in the Royal Free Hospital, and he knows how they work. And we will fix everything. We will arrange the room."

'It was impossible for me to pay for the treatment. I am a normal worker, an analyst programmer with computers. And the doctors in Portugal told us that probably our health authorities will not pay the treatment. I said, "OK. I'll try and pay myself. At least I have to try. Then we will see." But to start the process I have no money . . . because I have to go to London and I have to make a deposit of £12,000 on the first day, and I have not £12,000. So I talked with my boss, the manager in the factory where I work. He said, "It's a lot of money. I have to talk with our boss in Holland." And the boss in Holland said, "Yes, go on." And he lent me the money – £12,000, and then £6,000, and then £2,000 more. But then, after all the bureaucracy, our authorities decided to pay. So they sent back the money I paid before.

'The authorities pay for Eduardo and one person. Most people don't want to live in the hospital, so the authorities pay for a flat and food and electricity. Of course, they don't pay the Scalextric cars or the camera I bought for my son – or the telephone. But our boss authorized us to use the telephone in the factory. So when I am in London, my wife rings every day, and when she is in London I ring every day – one of the wonderful things that happened to us.

'I worked in the factory twelve years. So it is one third of my life. And it's more, because I do not have a timetable for work – I do not go to the factory at nine and finish at six. For example, I have one manager who sometimes tells me on Friday at a quarter to six, as we finish, that he needs his results on Monday at nine o'clock. So I have to work during the weekend. But he doesn't tell me to work during the weekend.

He only says, "Have a nice weekend – I need the results at nine o'clock on Monday." And that is funny in a way, because sometimes I would say to myself: this is not fair, because there are some workers working during the weekend and there is extra payment, and I work with them and I don't receive payment, and it's not fair . . . bla, bla, bla. Now I have the payment. And they are still paying my wages for one year.

'In two days and a half after we were told that Eduardo had leukaemia, we were in London. It was very quick. We had to talk with Eduardo to explain why we came here. He knows only that he has a problem called leukaemia, and he doesn't know anything else. We had to tell him that in London it was better than in Portugal, because the treatment was quicker. We thought it was three months, but we said to him: "It is better to spend one year in London – and probably we would have to spend more than a year in Portugal." So he doesn't worry. Even about the consequences. Sometimes he wants to know, but mostly not. But when he wants to know, I don't know how to answer.

'When we came to London it was horrible, horrible. We didn't know anything. We couldn't speak English. I told the doctors: "I put my son in your hands. At the end give me my son again. I want to go to Portugal with my son walking." And I trusted the doctors – doctors, nurses, professors, medicines, everything. And when you trust, the language is not a barrier.

'In Portugal they told me that the Royal Free was one of the best hospitals in the world to treat leukaemia. I came here without chances, and here they told me Eduardo had a chance, at least twenty per cent. I knew he had a chance because they explained everything. They spoke with me slowly and clearly, and I understood a lot of things – not everything, of course, because although I could read and write in English I could not speak. But the most difficult was to listen. It was horrible. Now it's not so bad.

'They were really careful, the way they talked to us. Step by step. They said, "You have to stay here six weeks, eight weeks – for chemotherapy." And I thought, "Chemotherapy, that's all, finished." So we finished the chemotherapy – and William was preparing for his transplant in the next room. And then, after that, or just before we finished, they said, "You have to go out for one week, and you have to come back again, and you have to stay, probably three, four months." I cried, because at the beginning I thought it was only eight weeks. But I didn't understand.'

CHAPTER 13

♦

As for William, his final block of chemotherapy – the treatment that irrevocably committed him to the transplant procedure – had now begun, under the anxious gaze of parents, doctors and nurses. A hundred miles away, at almost exactly the same moment, a related event was watched by another crowd of well-wishers. Jonathan Appleby, the youngest son of William's village schoolteacher, dived into the swimming pool in King's Lynn to cover the first lengths of a twenty-four-hour sponsored swim in aid of leukaemia research. After two months of organizing and negotiating with the authorities, Mrs Appleby had collected ten children between the ages of twelve and eighteen who were prepared to keep the swim going all through the night and the following day. She fixed eight o'clock as the starting time.

'That was when the club usually started, and for them to get the night over first, when they'd be flagging, would be best. As it was, they had a great time. They swam half-hour sessions each, one after the other. I think our family staggered home about three-thirty in the morning, after having the pool to ourselves for about two hours. But the pool staff stayed. They gave all their time free ... because, of course, they had to be there all the time.

'It was a tremendous distance. I think it was over eighty miles. The press were there for the start; and during the day, the public came in. We had just one lane at the side of the pool. We'd got leukaemia stickers all over the swimming pool. Rebecca, my daughter, stood at the door shaking her tin all day. We'd got balloons in the foyer that the leukaemia research people gave us, and parents were putting money in the tins for the balloons even though they were free. It was Whitsun, and a lovely sunny day. People were coming through all the time. One man went up to Rebecca and said, "I've had leukaemia and I've been cured: here's a fiver."

'Just as it finished, the Mayor of Wisbech arrived with a cheque for eighty pounds. We had some wine, and Rebecca had made a cake. Towards the end we were hoping to make four thousand lengths. The children had set their heart on a thousand pounds – they reckoned they could manage a hundred pounds each, but in the end it proved to be double – we were just a few pounds short of two thousand.

'It wasn't the adults. I organized the food and so on . . . but the children did all the work. They had the will to do it, and do it well. They all went round and collected – from school and college, and knocking on doors. And when the little swimmers knew the big swimmers were swimming, they all wanted to swim too. So we had to let them do half an hour or an hour's sponsored swim the same night. It was quite spontaneous.'

Sue was conscious of the fact that the sponsored swim was starting at the moment William's chemotherapy began. 'We hadn't forgotten about the swim. I can remember commenting on it. It meant something, that they were doing their swim at eight o'clock. Originally we were hoping that William was going to be there to swim himself. He'd been in remission, and he'd been swimming only the week before – the BBC filmed him – and he was certainly capable of swimming that day.'

The doctor chiefly responsible for looking after William day by day was Paul Roderick. It was his job to oversee the administration of William's chemotherapy, and to watch for side-effects.

'It was high-dose conditioning, designed to do two things: firstly, to eliminate any residual leukaemia (in combination with the radiotherapy still to come) – so you give high doses of drugs that kill off the leukaemic marrow, and all the normal marrow as well. But not only that; it's also designed to destroy as much of the patient's immunity as possible, so he won't reject the graft.

'Cyclophosphamide does both jobs. It's given in quite a high dose and it can cause problems – cystitis, bleeding from the bladder. So it's given with lots of fluids, bags of many litres of fluid a day, and you have to be very careful that the patient is passing that water out in the urine. We had to wake William up every hour to make sure he was still passing urine. We didn't want just to put it in, with nothing coming out. If you do that, people just blow up – it all ends in the lungs and they get very breathless. You have to be very careful how much you put in and how much you get out. Basically, it's to keep the bladder flushed through, so that the levels of the cyclophosphamide and the breakdown products of the cyclophosphamide don't damage the bladder. We also give another drug at the same time, which seems to protect the wall cells of the bladder.

'We've had very few problems, but if you give cyclophosphamide alone in that dose, a significant proportion of patients get bleeding from the bladder. That can be quite serious if the platelets in the blood, the clotting agents, are right down. Or alternatively, you can get clots which block the tube from the bladder. That's a problem, and a site for infection. So we need the second drug.'

No doctor enjoys turning someone who seems quite healthy into someone who seems quite sick. After his operations William was low and uncomfortable. He had a sore throat, and his neck hurt where the surgeon had made the cut to reach the main vein leading to the heart. As Dr Roderick knew, cyclophosphamide would make William feel sick.

'That can be distressing,' he says, 'particularly if you have a painful neck, and a painful backside from the auto-harvest of marrow. We try to fit things in conveniently, but sometimes we can't get everything booked to give the patient a three- or four-day break between things. It's obviously not ideal to start on conditioning when someone's just come back from theatre, but often that's the only way we can book it.

'Cyclophosphamide was given over an hour on Thursday evening, beginning at eight; and then the fluids and other drugs were given over the next twenty-three hours. So the next dose of cyclophosphamide was given on Friday evening – and then another session of infusion. By Saturday afternoon the fluids could be reduced, and the other, protective drug was stopped, so things got a bit easier. It was two days of being woken up, being sick, being in pain. We do try to alleviate all that with anti-sickness injections and painkillers; but William obviously still felt lousy.'

After his operations, at the beginning of his chemotherapy William was still drowsy from the anaesthetic. But it was only a temporary relief. 'From that day I was just going downhill all the time really. I felt bad. I wasn't used to that dose. It was a bigger dose, a lot bigger. And I had to have mouthwashes four times a day – they were very strong – and lozenges to suck.'

During William's chemotherapy, Sue was able to sleep in the bed next to his. 'He was low. He couldn't understand how on the morning of the operations he could wake up feeling so well – and now, to him, it must have seemed as if he was back to square one. I think he'd forgotten very quickly how he felt before, at Addenbrooke's. He knew he had to get worse before he got better; but he was homesick. He kept asking: "Why was I ever born?" Then he'd cry a little, and then he'd fall into a deep sleep. All Tim and I could do was reassure him that when he was well, he wouldn't say that. He said something that was very affecting. He said to Tim, "Dad, I'm sorry I've been such a lot of trouble to you." He was most concerned.'

The moment of William's transplant was now approaching. It was planned for the following Monday, 2 June. On that day the bone-marrow from Harriet, the donor, would be harvested and prepared; William would be given total body irradiation to eliminate the last of the leukaemia and complete the suppression of his immune system; and in the evening the transplant would be given.

On Saturday Tim drove back to Norfolk. He planned to collect Harriet from Sue's parents and bring her back to the hospital the next day, so that she would be ready for Monday's bone-marrow harvest. It was the end of the month and Tim needed to visit the shop in King's Lynn and sign the monthly cheques which his assistant, Claire Shewring, had ready for him.

On Sue's instructions, Harriet was allowed to pack whatever toys she wanted, along with her pyjamas and dressing-gown. No one wanted the donor to be upset. After Sunday lunch at the farm, Tim and Harriet set out. Harriet was talkative, a little nervous.

In hospital, Julia and the film crew were at work. They filmed one of the doctors telling William what to expect the next day.

Sue watched from behind the camera. 'William was feeling depressed and unwell, quite fed-up. When the filming was over the doctor left; but Julia still needed some shots of William listening. One of the crew sat on the bed and pretended to be the doctor. That really tickled William. He saw the funny side of it. It was enough to brighten him up – he never looked back that day at all.'

Finishing the film sequence took so long that Sue was taken by surprise at Harriet's arrival. 'I can remember Julia wishing she'd been ready to film as Harriet came up the corridor and saw me . . . she was so pleased to see me, her face shone. I shall never forget her face. She hugged me and she gave me some flowers – and as Julia said, you could never have repeated that. But then Julia did film her – just where we met, before she saw William.'

It was the first time Harriet had ever been in hospital, and she describes her first impressions: 'I was expecting bigger bedrooms. I was expecting more mothers and people. Sister Jordan asked, "Would you like to sleep on your own, or would you like to sleep with someone else?" So I said, "Could I sleep with somebody else, like a proper patient?" There was a girl with a broken leg I made friends with. Then there was my bed. Then there was a spare bed. And I met a girl called Angela, who kept coming into hospital with asthma.'

Harriet's bed was in an open ward opposite the nurses' desk, only a few yards from William's room in the corner of the block. After unpacking her night-things and her toy lion, Harriet went to visit William. He was beginning to feel a little better and was sitting up. This time the crew were prepared. The meeting was filmed as it happened. 'You're wearing your party dress,' said William. Then Harriet unpacked the things she had brought, presents from Grandma and Grandad, tapes and books, a Liverpool football team poster, a box of Maltesers which William distributed among the film-makers.

Harriet knew why she had been chosen as the bone-marrow donor, and what was going to happen: 'I was bigger than Edward, so they could take more to give to William; but with Edward they could only take less, because he's got a smaller one. Mine's more bigger. And if Edward had the bone-marrow taken, he's only got a little bit left . . . it might not grow again. But I'd have quite a bit left.'

About nine o'clock Harriet went to sleep. The noise of the open ward was disturbing, and Sue had to read with her and pretend to go to sleep too, until Harriet dropped off. Sue was no longer sleeping in William's room. She and Tim had a room of their own in the ward's central service-block.

About three o'clock the next morning Harriet woke up and went to look for Sue. 'She knew where our room was, and she knocked on the door. And rather than have her come in with us, I took her back and lay on her bed with her, thinking I'd get her back to sleep. But to be honest, at three or four in the morning the noise at the desk – which was just across the open passage-way – was just the same as in the middle of the day. The phone kept ringing, there was banging and clattering of trolleys. You'd never have thought it was night-time. Both Harriet and I tossed and turned, and we were most relieved when six a.m. came and they were bringing tablets and things round.

'About half past six Harriet went off to have a bath. I went with her. I would say she was still quite excited. At the desk, sister said, "Just pop this white gown on", and as we were walking to the bathroom Harriet announced that she was putting her knickers on. I said, "Well, they'd like you to put this gown on, and then you can put your dressing-gown on the top" – thinking that she was worried because the hospital gown was backless. And she said, "I'm putting my vest *and* my knickers on." Then I thought: ah, here's problem number one. She was quite adamant that she was having her vest and knickers on. Those were the first few tears. Once she got in the bath, she obviously realized that this was it. "They're going to ask me to do things I don't want to do." But in the end we got the gown on, and she went back to bed – until it was time for her pre-med before she went down to the operating theatre.'

Harriet has not forgotten how her mood changed in hospital. 'I wasn't frightened the first day, but I was the next day. I didn't take my pre-med. Dad spilt it all down me.'

The pre-med, designed to make patients relaxed and drowsy, was simply a little clear syrup in a measuring-pot. Sister Jordan gave it to Harriet to drink. Harriet refused. Tim picked her up. 'I took her to see William with it, and then we went for a walk; we ended up back at the entrance to the drugs room. I said, "Come on, Harriet, you've got to have it; open wide." She opened wide, I put it to her mouth, and she brushed it away and spilt it all down herself – which didn't best please Daddy. And Daddy restrained himself. It's the only time Harriet's had me in a position where I knew I'd got to restrain myself because of the company. A normal reaction would have been a slap.'

By this time Sue had gone back to William. 'I couldn't stand this fighting. I realized we were going to have problems. In the end they phoned Dr Simons, the anaesthetist; when he arrived, it was about half an hour after they'd first tried to give her the pre-med. She'd well and truly worked herself up. She was hysterical.'

Tim knew there was no alternative to force. 'It took four of us to hold her down. There was Dr Simons – and he'd been in the night before specially, to explain everything to Harriet – and Sue, and myself and Sister Jordan. Sister Jordan had spoken to Harriet the day before, as well, and told her what was going to happen.'

Sister Jordan was almost as upset as Sue and Tim. 'As a nurse, you always feel such a failure when things go wrong; but with children you can't predict. If you say, "Harriet, we're just going to give you some medicine", she may say, "Yes, all right" – but to get her to take it . . . Harriet's mouth would just close every time. Obviously, with any child who's having an operation we want to minimize the trauma; so we try to get the child's co-operation in any way we can. We rely on the fact that if they've fasted for, say, six hours, they're going to be thirsty; and certainly, at toddler age, they'll happily take a drink. But five, six, eight – if they know it's not a nice drink, sometimes there's no way they're going to take it.'

Dr Simons gave Harriet an injection of Valium, while, with the help of the others, Tim held her. 'It was just something I had to do to stop her struggling,' Tim says. 'I can remember as we pushed the bed down the corridor, Dr Simons said: "Well, that's the first full adult dose"; and he'd just about half emptied his syringe. He was giving her a little bit at a time, and by the time we got to the theatre he'd finished the syringe – double the adult dose.'

The semi-conscious Harriet was still crying as the trolley was wheeled into the operating theatre's ante-room.

'Look after Bumble-lion,' said Tim. 'Be a good girl.' A sob and a sniff.

'Don't worry,' said Sister Jordan to Sue. 'Don't worry. There's a good man in there. They're all good people.'

'I'm sure they are,' said Sue, now in tears herself.

'It won't take long. I'll take you round to recovery, where she'll come out.'

'I'll come up and see you later,' said Dr Simons from behind a mask. 'You'll need a good breakfast.'

Harriet was anaesthetized and wheeled into the theatre. Green sheets covered the whole of her body, except the area in which Malcolm Brenner was to work. As with William, he inserted a large hollow needle into Harriet's pelvis, to which a series of syringes could be attached. As the nurses rinsed the syringes in anti-coagulant to prevent the marrow from clotting, Dr Brenner took each in turn, inserted it into the needle, and then pulled the plunger up to draw the marrow out.

'We took just a teaspoonful of marrow at a time, only making one or two holes in the skin and moving the needle around underneath to locate different bits of marrow in the bone. We took bone-marrow from the cavities in the back of the hips first, and then from the front of the hips. We couldn't take more than about half a pint of marrow from someone Harriet's size – and as William was slightly larger than she was, that might have been a problem. But being so young, her marrow was likely to be very vigorous, well-populated with cells, so we hoped there would be enough to graft William adequately.

'It looks a very painful procedure. People always ask: "Doesn't it hurt when they wake up?" But in fact it causes little discomfort. Patients usually complain of stiffness for a day or two – that's about the limit. The marrow that we take is soon made up by the body. It's a very small portion of the total marrow contained within the body – and it doesn't cause them any problems.'

The marrow was collected in a sterile transparent plastic bag and taken to the laboratories for treatment. First, the marrow, the progenitor cells, had to be separated from the mature cells of the blood. The contents of the bag were fed into a centrifuge. As it spun, the centrifuge separated the cells into different layers – the densest cells finding their way to the outside of the centrifuge. The layer containing the bone-marrow could then be piped off.

But that was not all. As we pointed out earlier, transplanted bone-marrow performs two functions. It rescues the patient by providing him with replacement cells to produce blood and build up a new immune system, his own having been destroyed by drugs and radiation. But transplanted bone-marrow also attacks any leukaemic cells still remaining in the recipient. A bone-marrow transplant, therefore, itself helps to prevent the leukaemia recurring. However, there is a snag.

The cells contained in bone-marrow are not all of one type. One group, called T-cells, have the characteristic that they attack any alien material. If transplanted, they attack not only leukaemic cells but also the recipient's healthy cells, causing 'graft versus host' disease, which kills many transplant patients. To prevent that happening, most of the T-cells must be eliminated from the transplanted bone-marrow.

For that purpose, antibodies – structures which themselves have the property of recognizing alien cells – were added to Harriet's bone-marrow. They recognized the T-cells of Harriet's immune system, and fastened on to them. These antibodies are grown in a tissue culture, or else in the abdomens of rats and mice; but the strange fact is that since the immune system is common to all living things from invertebrates upwards (in varying degrees of sophistication), it does not matter if these antibodies come from a non-human source. Even sea-anemones on a rock share the same basic immune system. The function the antibodies were performing was to decide whether Harriet's T-cells were its own or not, self or non-self.

By themselves, the antibodies would not have destroyed Harriet's T-cells. To achieve that, serum derived from baby rabbits had to be added to Harriet's bone-marrow. This contained factors which reacted with the antibodies from the mice and killed Harriet's T-cells. Then a phosphate saline solution was used to wash away the loose proteins derived from the added animal matter, leaving the surface of the live, non-T-cells clean. Finally, the live cells were separated out in preparation for the moment of transplant.

To Malcolm Brenner, the technique of depleting bone-marrow of its T-cells is a half-way house between doing nothing and an ideal system of using human antibodies.

'At the moment it's a bit of a zoo – mice and rats and rabbits: it reminds me of *Macbeth*. People would very much like to make human monoclonal antibodies. You would take cells from human genes, insert them into rodent cells and grow them in a tissue culture. Then you would have a nice clean transplant procedure by which you would give the marrow along with an injection of human antibody which would by itself kill the unwanted T-cells. You could do it in one go; and the residue would simply be disposed of by the recipient's body in the ordinary way. That's coming. A lot of people are working on it, including the Royal Free. But the procedure is technically more complex. Small abnormalities can lead to problems.

'The present system works well on the whole, though there have been times when we've run into trouble. We found that an antibody which normally destroys ninety-eight or ninety-nine per cent of the T-cells in the donated bone-marrow was only killing eighty-five or ninety per cent. Somehow or other the cells that were growing the antibodies were damaged, or the production of the antibodies didn't go quite right, and their efficiency was impaired. We had awful trouble with 'graft versus host' disease. For two or three patients it was very bad news. We realized what was happening almost at once, but once you're committed to treating bone-marrow, and on the way, there's not much you can do. You can't just prolong the antibody treatment, because the longer you treat the marrow, the less viable it becomes. If you add more antibodies, or different antibodies, there are big problems in that the graft itself may be rejected.

'But with T-cell depletion, there are other factors to be considered. Even when it goes smoothly, it's not absolutely straightforward: by eliminating T-cells from the donated marrow, you reduce the risk of 'graft versus host' disease; but because T-cells are good at attacking leukaemic cells as foreign, by eliminating T-cells you increase the risk of the leukaemia recurring. Some people who do very intensive T-cell depletion, and eliminate the very last of the T-cells, get higher relapse rates.

'But with our regime of T-cell depletion, we seem to produce only a very slight weakening of the anti-leukaemic effect. Certainly the number of relapses hasn't been any greater than with untreated marrow. And the overall benefit of avoiding the terrible problems of "graft versus host" disease outweighs any increased risk of the cancer coming back.

'You have to strike a balance. You have to avoid 'graft versus host' disease by taking out most of the T-cells, while not taking out so many that you eliminate the anti-leukaemic activity. If you measure the risk of the cancer recurring, you probably do worst if you get your own marrow back, because to the marrow the leukaemia seems least foreign; better if you get an identical twin's marrow; better still if you get a sibling's marrow, even if it has been T-cell depleted; probably best of all if you get a sibling's marrow which hasn't been T-cell depleted.

'But against that, the risk of dying from 'graft versus host' disease is greatest with a sibling's marrow which hasn't been T-cell depleted; less with a sibling's marrow which has been T-cell depleted; less still with an identical twin; and least of all with your own.'

When Sue and Tim left Harriet at the entrance to the operating theatre, they knew they would not be able to collect her for a couple of hours. Tim felt frustrated by Harriet's disobedience. 'Everything had gone according to plan. It would have been so simple for her just to take her pre-med.'

Sue was still trying to hold back her tears. 'William would have just drunk it. But Harriet was frightened – and she'd been so good. I I didn't feel as if Harriet had let us down; but it was a bad moment . . . it certainly made things a bit tense. And William knew what was going on . . . he'd seen Harriet with Tim. Here we were, transplant day, with a bright, happy boy . . . and we've got Harriet sobbing away.

'Dr Simons said, "Go and have a good breakfast" . . . but the thought of it! Tim and I went straight back to William's room. We were cleaning it – we hadn't been back very long – when Tim's sister, Ann, turned up . . . which was lovely, the biggest surprise of all. She said she'd come for the day to give us a hand. I hadn't thought how we would cope with two children in different places – we just presumed we would manage. But the minute I saw her I felt relieved. Plus the fact that, in that particular week, we hadn't had many visitors. William was quite happy to sit and chat to Auntie Ann, while Tim and I fetched Harriet from the recovery-room together and spent a little time with her. I thought she'd have been knocked out for the afternoon, but as we walked down the corridor to recovery, we heard sniffs . . . I couldn't believe she was still sobbing, but she was. She was in the same state when we collected her as she was when we left her. And then I thought: Crumbs, we've got the whole day now. She'd got a bad back, a drip in the back of her hand and a sore throat. When she reached the ward, she just put her head on the pillow and went on sobbing and moaning in her sleep.'

Tim was witness to the next minor crisis. 'The drip in her hand was for a blood transfusion. It was held by a splint on her arm. She pulled her arm out of the splint and we had blood everywhere. Dr Simons, the anaesthetist, was called again, and he had to fix another drip. He gave her an injection in her leg to calm her down.'

Sue eventually left Tim and went down to the canteen to have lunch and a chat with Ann. When it was Tim's turn to eat, Sue took his place by Harriet's bed to make sure she didn't pull the drip out again. 'She was sleeping very restlessly. During the afternoon she woke up enough to read a letter from Gran. She said, "Silly Gran's written it twice" – she was still seeing double. And then she began colouring Snoopy, and Snoopy kept moving up and down the page.'

CHAPTER 14

About four o'clock on the day Harriet's bone-marrow was collected, William was taken down to the radiotherapy department. His trolley was wheeled past the open ward where Harriet was recovering, so that they could be filmed waving to each other as he went past. Once again, to create a truthful image that told its own story on film, normal practice was slightly modified. William's trolley was pushed the long way round the ward; while Harriet's bed was shifted out from the wall into the centre of the room to give the cameraman the right angle.

The purpose of William's journey was total body irradiation (TBI) – the process by which X-rays would be used to kill any remaining leukaemic cells and to complete the suppression of his own immune system. That would very greatly reduce the risk that he might reject Harriet's marrow.

Tim and Sue followed William down. Sue tried to put Harriet out of her mind. 'Tim's brother, Duffy, had arrived unexpectedly during the afternoon, so we left him and Ann to look after Harriet – though she hardly knew they were there. William was quite chatty and cheerful. From having been so ill from the chemotherapy on Friday and Saturday, by Monday he was nearly back to the state he had been in before. When we got to the radiation-room we had to put on gowns, masks and gloves – like the film crew. That was a new experience. By the time we were dressed up, William was off the trolley and sitting in the chair, on a platform. He was high up. It was as though he was on an execution chair. The fact that he was raised up . . . the whole thing had that feeling about it. He was getting prepared to be executed . . . a band round his forehead, a little white vest, all in white.'

Half-a-dozen radiographers set William in the fetal position, attached the dose-measuring discs to his body and packed the bolus bags round him. To keep them secure, they were fastened with ties. The band round his forehead held his head steady against the chair, centred with the help of a measuring-stick.

Overseeing everything was Dr Teresa Tate. 'The headband was mostly for William's comfort, because it's quite difficult to keep your head in exactly the same position. And if it's bound securely to the back, you can afford to relax. You're likely to drop off, especially if you're well sedated, and your head will loll. William also needed to keep the mid-line of his whole body in the same plane, not rocking from one side to the other. It isn't easy. You get very uncomfortable . . . cramps in your legs. And if you move the bolus bags, the dose will be affected. So the strapping was just to support William's legs and make him feel more secure.

'Of course we couldn't put bolus bags round his head because they wouldn't have stayed there, though we could have put one round his neck. But the head is much narrower than the rest of the body. So instead of bolus bags we used a piece of metal, lead, hanging in the path of the X-ray beam, between the source and William's head, so that it cast a shadow on the head and neck. We didn't use it during the test dose. We simply calculated how much more had gone to William's head than to his shoulders, and therefore how thick the piece of lead should be to make sure the dose to the head was equal to the dose to the rest of the body.

'The lead was hung from the ceiling on the same contraption that also held a piece of plastic sheeting in the path of the beam. The plastic was to alter the characteristic of the whole X-ray beam. When very high-energy radiation beams penetrate something, they don't deposit a hundred per cent of the dose until they get below the surface. That's usually helpful in patients who are receiving radiation, because the skin doesn't get so badly damaged. But in William's case we wanted the skin to get the full dose, because the leukaemic cells were circulating there. The plastic sheeting began to absorb the radiation, so that by the time it reached William's skin he was getting a hundred per cent of the effect.'

William took the preparations calmly. He neither looked nor behaved like a child fighting a decisive battle with death. There was even a little colour in his cheeks. His recollections of that day are detailed and fresh in his mind: 'I remember being geared up for TBI. I wasn't allowed to move. There was a big strap that went round me, and a vest – I had a string vest to hold the probes – and polystyrene bags packed in. Hands crossed on my knees, with a vomit-tray on top.'

Every radiotherapy department has its own system of giving radiation. The conventional method is to give it over a number of days or weeks. The idea is to let the normal cells recover between doses. Tumour cells, being more sensitive to radiation, recover less well. So after, say, a five-week course, the patient has no tumour cells and a normal population of healthy cells. Similarly, some departments give TBI over a period of two or three days. Teresa Tate takes a different view.

'It's true that if you give TBI in several doses you need less careful monitoring each time because you can correct slight errors at the next session, whereas if you do it all at once you have to get it right first time. And from the patients' point of view, they might prefer it, because smaller doses don't make them sick. But it's disruptive for the department to have to make the radiation-room as sterile as possible six or seven times instead of once – as soon as radiation starts, the patient's immune system is under attack and the patient has to be barrier-nursed and protected from infection. It's our experience that the overall relapse rate is worse when radiation is given in small doses. Not everyone agrees with us.'

When everything was ready, everyone except William left the radiation-room. Sue watched as the switches were turned on. For her, radiotherapy was a new experience. 'You saw the red flashing lights and the "Danger, No Entry" sign on the door, and the radiation symbol. And that was your child in there. It was too dangerous for anyone else to be in there, but your child was sitting right in the middle of it.'

William felt isolated. 'All I could see was the inside of this room. The lights were down . . . I don't think there was very much light. There was some kind of intercom, and they could see me on the TV, but I couldn't see them. I remember listening to some tapes I borrowed off my Grandad – seventy-five songs that had been to Number One, a compilation of hits.'

In the narrow control-room outside, Dr Tate and her staff monitored the progress of the radiation. It was administered in short, separately calculated doses, and took between forty-five minutes and an hour altogether.

'There's no sensation,' says Dr Tate. 'You don't actually feel anything. But nausea will usually begin before it's over. William was obviously lonely, a bit frightened. For most patients it's a totally new experience, which has had years of bad publicity. The overall impression is that it's going to be terrible. That's one of the advantages of a test dose – we can demonstrate that we don't do anything that immediately makes the patient ill. But it's a long time, and it's alarming to hear the machine working . . . buzzing and whining. And you begin to feel uncomfortable and you want to wriggle about. And then the patient does begin to feel unwell and sick, and that can suggest all sorts of unthinkable possibilities. Once you've had the TBI, you can't say, "I'm sorry, I'm not sure we ought to have done this." You have to go on. You have to have the transplant, and it's got to take, for you to be OK . . . and sitting there on your own can bring all that home to you.'

Each dose lasted three or four minutes. For Dr Tate that was a safe-guard.

'Because of having to divide the dose into small bits, it's totally impossible to give, say, double the dose by mistake. The clock on the machine can only be set to a certain maximum number of units – just over nine hundred. So we gave William separate doses of nine hundred, with a little left over for the last dose at the end. So we may reset the clock seven or eight times. William also had a probe attached to his skin, which gave a direct reading of the radiation; and in the beam behind him on the wall was a big dose-reading machine as well, with a read-out on the control-panel outside. That acted as a check on the cumulative dose. You can't afford to make mistakes – that's why several people are involved: two radiographers recording and a third actually setting the machine, and being told how much; a physicist reading all the dose-meters, and somebody comparing what she's call-ing out against the dose we've calculated we should have reached. Afterwards we use the test-discs as a final check.'

At first, William did not seem to have much to complain about. 'It felt strange. I started to itch, and I wanted to scratch my toes. But the first half went fine.'

After twenty-five minutes the radiation was switched off, and the radiographers went into the radiation-room to turn William round. In the second block, William started to get dozy. 'I didn't let myself sleep. I felt a bit sick.'

Sue found it upsetting to watch. 'I didn't like to see him strapped in and trapped. It was frightening. And yet I knew that I wanted and needed to get back to Harriet. I was torn – which way to go? In the end I was glad I went to Harriet.'

The closed-circuit television screens at the end of the control-panel gave only a blurred monochrome picture of William's face. Through the speaker could be heard the sound of his retching. Once again the radiation was switched off. Some radiographers went in to reassure him and help him to be sick into the vomit-tray balanced on his knees.

Tim went with them. 'I told him, "The longer you can last out, the less trouble you're going to have. They'll only have to fasten you up again. You may as well last through it." I was frightened he was going to make it worse for himself. It was much better that he should be brave enough to get through all of it at once.'

Dr Tate gave the word for the treatment to start again. 'William was obviously distressed, lonely, a bit frightened. But we'd try very, very hard not to let him get out of the chair, however much he wanted to; because we'd have to put him back into exactly the same position, and it would have got more and more difficult as he got increasingly ill and upset. We also find that the less a patient is disturbed, the greater their tolerance and the less their sickness will be. Really, William was remarkable for being so calm.'

William wanted to keep going until the end. 'Three-quarters of the way through I was a bit miserable. If the worst came to the worst, I would have to ask them to stop – I got quite near to that ... perhaps ninety-five per cent.'

Tim stayed close by. For Dr Tate it was helpful to have a parent like Tim to jolly William along through the last period. 'Some parents – I have to say, more often foreign parents than the stoical English – get so distressed that they make it worse for the child, and we have to ban them. Tim and William could talk to each other, though it was difficult to hear exactly what William was saying. You could hear cries of distress, but quite often you couldn't pick out the words. There was a microphone in the room, but not right in front of William. And you can't have radio transmitters in the room. It's always difficult because of having to contain the X-rays. Every department I've worked in has had a sound system that was rather unsatisfactory.'

At the end of an hour, the radiation was switched off for the last time. William was crying, and as the last indignity, which he most wanted to forget, he had wet himself.

CHAPTER 15

◆

Initially, Dr Tate had been rather unwilling to allow William's total body irradiation to be filmed. By the kind of accident common in film-making, the general consent of the hospital authorities to the project of making a film (and the enthusiasm of the haematology department, which was chiefly responsible for bone-marrow transplants) had been assumed to include the consent of the radiotherapy department. Dr Tate was not too pleased when it appeared that the BBC was taking her co-operation for granted. She also had perfectly reasonable fears that the presence of a film crew might be intrusive and distracting. In the end she agreed to the crew's presence. William was filmed as he was being prepared; while the X-ray machine was switched on, he was filmed via the television monitors in the control-room.

After about forty-five minutes, when William had been showing signs of distress for some time, Julia McLaren judged that it would be tactful to withdraw the crew. I disagreed. I felt that it was our job to go on recording what happened, even at the risk of causing irritation and anxiety. Only if our presence began to have an effect on William's treatment should we leave. In principle, I may have been right. I was angry at the time that we were missing the climax of one of the crucial episodes in William's story. In practice, I was wrong. When the film came to be put together, it turned out that, like the display of violence, the display of suffering on the screen can become gratuitous and un-necessary long before it has reached the extremes of real life. We had no need of more explicit scenes of William's reaction to radiation.

That was the closest Julia and I came to having a row. We were also extraordinarily lucky in our relations with other people, not only with William, Sue and Tim and the rest of their family, but with all the people we met in hospital. There was only one occasion on which we were asked not to film. One of the doctors felt that the presence of the camera might be distressing to Sue and Tim while they were all discussing the effects of TBI on William immediately after the treat-ment. As we discovered later, Sue and Tim were by that time so used to us that the ban was really unnecessary. We were all becoming friends.

About half past six on Monday, 2 June, William returned from the radiation-room to his own room in the corner of Riddell Ward. Sue was there to see him in. 'His room had been completely changed. My bed had come out. The room had been cleaned. He had clean bedlinen – it had already been changed once that day, but it was changed again. It suddenly seemed more sterile – lots of his bits and pieces had been taken out, anything that wasn't new. That's when Charge Nurse David did his clear-up with the student nurses. The room that William left didn't seem like his room when we went back. It was a clean, sterile room – and more spacious. That was a shock. I expected to go back to the same old room – even though I knew I couldn't sleep there any more.'

William was still retching and vomiting from the effects of radiation on the membranes of his gut. After a while the sickness passed off, and Sue and Tim left William alone. Looking back now, Sue finds their behaviour almost shocking.

'It sounds awful, doesn't it? William's transplant was about to happen and we were outside his room with the film crew. We had coffee – I remember Jane, Julia's production assistant, making it. We were discussing the day. William was on his own; he was very sleepy. We were watching him through the window. Then we went back in, and Dr Roderick arrived. A student nurse was there, and David. We were all in aprons and gloves and masks.'

Paul Roderick carried with him the circular transparent plastic bag from the centrifuge in which Harriet's bone-marrow had been separated out and processed. He drew the almost clear liquid out of the bag into a large syringe, perhaps an eighth of a pint. Then he unplugged the end of the Hickman catheter on William's chest and fixed the syringe on to the end of it.

'If you'll just unclamp the catheter,' he said to the nurse. 'And if someone will just time me . . .'

William, though sleepy, was conscious. Propped up on the pillows, he watched. 'The last words I can remember when the bone-marrow went in . . . Mum said, "This is what we've been waiting for, William." And they slowly timed it, and got the bone-marrow into the blood-stream. And that began working straight away.'

Tim picked up the circular centrifuge bag and put it in the sink in the shower-room in the corner of William's room. 'I didn't mention it to anybody. I just picked it up and thought: I'll keep that as a souvenir.'

Dr Roderick went on pushing the plunger slowly down the syringe. Tim came back into the room. Sue watched the transplant continue. 'It took ten minutes. It was a complete anticlimax. The big thing had been the radiation.'

Tim could hardly believe what was happening. 'I couldn't believe that that injection was going to save William's life . . .'

'But that was it.'

'That was it. *That . . . was . . . it.* That's what it was all about, a syringeful of –'

'– when that went in, he'd had a bone-marrow transplant. And And outside, in the barrier-room, Tim and I could see Fernanda, little Eduardo's mother. She'd come out of his room, and was watching through the window. And that night she rang up big Eduardo – he'd had to go back to Portugal to see about payment for the treatment – and said: "I've just seen a little boy have a transplant . . . the boy from the North" (Eduardo thought we must be Scottish or Irish), "William, in the room next door, has just had a bone-marrow transplant. There's nothing to it." But of course she didn't know anything about T B I, or anything like that. A good job she didn't realize that's what little Eduardo was going to have. She had no idea.'

An injection, even one through a tube into one of the veins leading to the heart, seems such a simple, familiar procedure. Before I met William and began to follow his case, I had imagined something far more dramatic and threatening. I even had fantastic images of surgeons cutting sections of marrow-bone from a donor's leg and inserting them into the recipient – and I do not expect I am the only person to have been so mistaken. Even doctors had misconceptions to begin with, as Malcolm Brenner recalls.

'When they first started doing transplants, they didn't realize you could get the marrow to repopulate by putting it into the veins and letting it recirculate. What they did was drill holes into the marrow cavities and inject it straight into them. The other way they did it was to inject the arteries which fed the marrow cavities . . . so it went *Voomph!* straight into the marrow. But there's no need to do that. The transplanted marrow finds its own way through the normal circulation of the blood.

'You infuse about half a wine-glassful – but most of what you infuse ends up not in the marrow. You take about one per cent of the donor's marrow – because most of what you take is blood – and you put that into the recipient; and probably only about one per cent of the one per cent actually ends up in his marrow cavities. Most of the rest of it is filtered out by the lungs, and by the kidneys, the liver and the spleen. If you listen to the lungs afterwards, you sometimes hear these horrible crackles . . . with all the cells that have ended up there, blocking the lungs. It's amazing how the infused marrow grows at all.

'What happens is that a very small percentage by chance escapes all the clearance mechanisms, which treat the transplant as waste, as something which is not meant to be there. The transplant's not exactly in prime condition, taken out of someone's body, treated with all these chemicals and drugs and serum and things. It's all a bit clogged, and it looks to the body as though it's damaged tissue which has got into the system. But a bit of it escapes, it gets through, and it goes into the recipient's marrow cavities.

'On the surface of the progenitor cells [the primitive, undeveloped cells that make up the transplant] there are recognition sites; while in the marrow cavities there are support cells with probes that can pick out the recognition sites on the progenitor cells. If by chance the progenitor cells end up there, they lock on and fix themselves. One per cent of one per cent . . . I don't know of any other organ of which you can transplant such a small quantity, and get it to regenerate.

'In that respect your blood-making system is like an earthworm – cut a bit off and it grows again. It's a shame you can't do that with the rest of the body. It really is extraordinary. It's not like having a finger cut off and grow again: it's like losing your arm up to the shoulder and having the whole thing grow back. That's not an exact parallel, but the degree of differentiation of re-grown cells is the same . . . from one early cell to all the different types of cell that make up your immune and blood systems. One cell is enough. It's like being born again . . . without the marrow the body is an empty husk.'

When the transplant was over, I interviewed Sue and Tim on camera. Did Sue think the worst was over?

'I didn't really know how I felt. But I did say I thought the worst was over. And then Tim qualified that.'

'I thought the worst was over – from the point of view of the transplant treatment, obviously. But otherwise it was unpredictable. For me, mentally, I expected the next fortnight to be the hardest, waiting to see if the graft had taken or not. Nick asked what I was looking forward to, and I said, "A little boy running round in his garden again." And Sue said she wanted William home for his tenth birthday, 27 July.'

By nine-thirty in the evening Harriet had been settled down, and William was dozing. The night nurse, Jackie, came in to sit with William. Tim and Sue were hungry. Before eating, they telephoned all William's grandparents and Ken Doran, their doctor at home, to give them the news. Then they had a pizza.

'Tim and I had both eaten at mid-day, but we'd had nothing since then. Late that night, bearing in mind that I'd been on the go since about three o'clock in the morning with Harriet, I was really starving. We had a giant-sized pizza in our room. That took us up to midnight, and then we went back to see William. And, of course, we had to put on plastic aprons again, and masks over our mouths and noses, and rubber gloves. Jackie was there. She was watching for any reaction to the transplant – the shakes or whatever, a bit like when he reacted to the platelets at Addenbrooke's. But basically she was going to take William's temperature and blood pressure every half-hour through the night. She suggested that Tim and I could both go to bed – that was about a quarter to one – and she'd call us if there was any problem. So we went off to bed, quite happy; and we did go to sleep – which I was surprised about. We were shattered.'

CHAPTER 16

About half past seven the next morning there was a knock on Tim and Sue's door. It was Harriet. Sue could hardly believe it was morning. 'You never knew what time of day or night it was in that place. I couldn't get dressed quickly enough to go and see how William was. Jackie told me that he had had a really good night, and had been a model patient. He had felt sick, but he hadn't had any problems with his temperature.'

William was lucky. As Sue knew, the shock of a bone-marrow transplant sometimes causes shaking, wheeziness, fever – even a collapse of the patient's blood pressure. 'It was a great anticlimax, really. You expect your child to be looking desperately ill after the transplant. You go in next morning, and there he is sitting up in bed. So Jackie went off-duty and we carried on with cleaning the room and so on.

'We also had to see to William's mouthwashes and lozenges. The previous week he'd had some very powerful mouthwashes – but they were very nasty. So William's consultant on the ward, Dr Prentice, said, "If I give you something that tastes nicer, do you promise to do it more often?" And William said, "Great! Yes!" So that meant eight mouthwashes a day, and eight lozenges to put under the tongue – William went to sleep with one under his tongue the first night. They worried me. I had a vision that, having had this transplant, he would choke on a lozenge while he was asleep. He had sterilization tablets three or four times a day, and they made him sick.'

Dr Brenner made sure everyone understood the medical routine that follows a transplant.

'The big problem after a transplant, before the marrow regenerates, is infection, mostly from bacteria or fungi living in your own body or on the skin. You carry them with you, and the radiation won't have killed them . . . they're very insensitive to it. Normally they're kept in check by the white cells, but if you lose the white cells, they tend to overgrow.

'The awkward fact is that though we can maintain the supply of red cells and platelets by transfusions, we can't do the same thing with white cells – either neutrophils, white blood cells, or lymphocytes, white cells of the immune system. Only a very small proportion of the white cells the body needs actually circulate in the blood. Most of them are stuck to the walls of the blood-vessels or elsewhere in the tissue. And in the circulating blood they have a very short life – about twenty-four hours. So even if you took all a person's blood and gave it to someone else, their white-cell count would be very, very low. The only way you can boost the white-cell count is by taking white cells from someone with another type of leukaemia, chronic granulocyitic leukaemia, which creates a hundred times or more the normal number of white cells. You irradiate it first, so it doesn't transmit leukaemia. But it's not a common process, because it doesn't work very well. It's a last resort.

'What we normally do to lessen the risk from the organisms carried by the body is to give antibiotics by mouth. They aren't absorbed, but they sterilize the gut – and we give anti-fungal agents as well, which are horrible.

'But despite our best efforts, almost everybody does get an infection. In fact ninety per cent of post-transplant patients get infections at some stage; and of those, ten per cent die – though most deaths occur later. In the early stages, the usual course of events is that during the first week nothing happens; the second week you get an infection; the third week you're all right.

'Normally in medicine you are taught not to treat temperatures, signs of infection, unless and until you know why they're there – because they're often mild and trivial, or they're caused by viruses, which antibiotics can't kill. And if you do prescribe, you don't want to give antibiotics to try to cover everything: you want to use an antibiotic that can kill the particular organism you've got. So you're taught to find out what infection you've got, and where, and then treat it. After bone-marrow transplants, it's the exact opposite. As soon as there's a hint of infection, you have to treat it. And you have to treat it with antibiotics that cover as wide a spectrum as you possibly can ... because without the white cells to defend you, even the most trivial infection can be overwhelming within hours.

'But the medical armoury has only so many "blunderbuss" anti-biotics. We keep on having to introduce new ones. There's a rolling programme of fourth- and fifth-generation drugs. An individual patient can't run through the whole armoury – usually; though it does some-times happen with an organism called pseudomonas. That grows all over the place, even in vases of flowers, and if it gets into your body it can be very resistant to antibiotics.'

Infection can also reach a post-transplant patient from outside his room. To minimize the risk, William was once again isolated from the outside world, but more strictly than ever before. Everyone going into his room had to wear mask, apron and gloves. Every object taken in had to be disinfected first. Even a box of tissues had to be sprayed. And everything in the room was scrupulously cleaned and disinfected every day.

William slept well the night after his transplant. But next morning, dozy and feeling slightly sick, he wasn't hungry. To prevent him losing weight as he had done at Addenbrooke's, Dr Brenner prescribed nourishment through a drip into William's Hickman catheter.

'We give feeding because a lot of people get diarrhoea and nausea from the drugs and radiation. The marrow is the most sensitive organ to radiation – so sensitive that the patient's own marrow has been destroyed – but another sensitive organ is the intestine. Any organ that's constantly replicating itself, constantly dividing, producing new cells, is going to be very vulnerable to anything that kills dividing cells, like cyclophosphamide and radiation. And after the marrow, the gut is the most rapidly dividing organ, because you're constantly shedding bits of your gut – it's turning over the whole time – and so it gets damaged by the radiation and doesn't absorb nourishment very well. So even if you're not feeling sick and you haven't got diarrhoea, and you can eat and keep food down, it doesn't get taken up into the body very well. People can lose a lot of weight.

'The feed consists of a mixture of partially digested proteins, carbohydrates, fats, vitamins, minerals – similar to the food your gut would normally be absorbing. But the manufacturers have done all the pre-digestion for you in stainless steel vats. Sometimes they start with synthetic amino-acids and join them together. Sometimes they start with animal or vegetable proteins and carbohydrates and break them down. They go straight into the bloodstream from the drip, whereas normally they would come out through the walls of the gut; to the body, it seems as if you've just digested them.'

During the course of the day after William's transplant, Eduardo Cunha moved out of the corner room next door. Eduardo and his mother, Fernanda, were to spend a week's convalescence, between blocks of chemotherapy, in a flat near the hospital. Eduardo's father was in Portugal, sorting out the financial arrangements, but he had seen the effect of Eduardo's treatment before he left: 'They explained that with myeloid leukaemia, they have to use much stronger drugs. So he spent a long time vomiting, with diarrhoea. It was dreadful, because all the time – during the day, during the night – he had diarrhoea and was vomiting. The first course of chemotherapy was really, really bad.'

Within half an hour of Eduardo's leaving, his place was taken by Helen Kitsa, a twelve-year-old from Greece. She was suffering from chronic myeloid leukaemia. With her were her father, Vasil, and her sixteen-year-old sister, Angeliki. Angeliki was to be the donor of the bone-marrow for the transplant for which Helen was being prepared. Their mother was still in Greece, looking after the five other children in the family.

Vasil and his daughters had had an anxious time. Vasil was not well off; and the Greek government, like the Portuguese government in Eduardo's case, had agreed to pay for Helen's transplant, in two instalments of £30,000. But when Helen arrived in England for preparatory chemotherapy, they found that the first instalment had been delayed, and the treatment could not begin until it had arrived.

The visitors were billeted with a Greek government interpreter – an arrangement neither side enjoyed. Vasil was not of Greek origin. He came originally from Romania. Tim and Sue felt that, as a Romany and a scrap-dealer, he was treated by the interpreter with a certain disdain. Once in hospital, he and his daughters found communication very difficult. They spoke little or no English, and the interpreter could not always be on hand. The hospital staff spoke no Greek. But now at last the transplant was only six days away.

Once again, it was difficult for William to make contact with his neighbour. He was too weak to get out of bed, so he was unable to stand at his door and look through the glass, across the corner of the barrier-room to where Helen could be seen behind her own door. But since William's radiation his bed had been moved into the space where his mother's bed had been before, hard up against the internal window which looked into the barrier-room. If William leant to the left and peered through this internal window, he could just see into Helen's room. The two children were able to wave, and over the days an acquaintance was struck up.

While William was dozing through the first forty-eight hours after his transplant, Harriet was fully recovered from the shock of giving her marrow.

'I enjoyed the days after I gave my bone-marrow. I said, "I don't want to go home."

'On the other side of the ward there was a boy. His dad came and he started moaning that he wanted to go home. And he got smacked. The next day his dad came to take him home, and he didn't want to. After that there was a spare bed; and then there was a girl called Clare, and she was my best friend in that room. I used to have breakfast on her bed, and the next day she'd have breakfast on my bed. She was always ringing her mum. She was all on her own . . . she was looking after herself. She was at least twelve. She was quite lonely before I came, but she was cheerful when we made friends. We went down in the lift to the shop to get something to eat; and she asked me to paint my nails in different colours.

'The person next door to me had a broken leg, and I started hopping into bed with her. We used to have games. Clare would hop in as well. And then next door there was this room with a boy crying at night, a little baby boy – it was dreadful. I couldn't get to sleep when he started crying. And there was this little baby girl, one year old, who pulled her drip out. She cried quite a lot.

'I went to the school in the ward. I stayed an extra day so that I could go twice. We'd been talking about eggs. So the teacher said: "About eggs – you can cook with eggs." So we thought we'd start to cook. We made biscuits. And I wasn't allowed to eat them in the car going home; so when I got back to Grandma's, they'd gone stale.'

Tim's brother, Michael, and Erica arrived to take Sue and Harriet home. This was the start of Sue's longer home visits; she felt that she could safely stay from Wednesday, when Harriet was discharged, until the following Saturday. William seemed so much better than she and Tim had ever dared hope, and she was anxious to see Harriet settled at home. There were no problems; Harriet returned to school – 'quite the hero, as you can imagine,' Sue says. 'She was fine.'

Tim was left on his own with William. He could see that William didn't want to do much. 'He became a little snail and wanted to crawl into his shell. He watched football. He played cards, but he couldn't concentrate for long. He was quiet the first few days. I was drawing him. I'd been drawing him since the chemotherapy started; and I drew flowers and things, as well – pen-and-ink sketches. And then on Tuesday, the day after the transplant, I painted a Care-Bear for Harriet. When she came out of school in the morning, it was on her wall. I got permission from Sister Jordan.'

When Charge Nurse David saw the painting, he did not approve. He told Tim that painting was not really allowed. 'It's an either-or situation. Either you do it or you don't. Tim's painting was very small. My idea for the future is to decorate the whole wall – but it will be something that is consistent. To have someone's personal style somewhere and then find he can't finish it off completely . . . that's not my idea. I know Tim's work is excellent – I've seen some of it – and if he could do it all, then he's welcome to come and do it.'

Sue returned to London on Saturday in time to watch Dr Roderick give William his daily examination. 'He would listen to his chest, look in his mouth for any sores – the minute there was a spot, it was a mouth swab. One day William did have a slight sore, but that was the only time. And he'd look at the palms of his hand and the soles of his feet. It seemed funny the first day, but they were looking for a rash – that's the first sign of 'graft versus host' disease. And Dr Roderick would always peel off the circular plastic cover where the Hickman was curled up on William's chest to see if there were any signs of infection; and he'd take a blood sample, to see if William needed platelets or blood. That was the basic routine; and we were always pleased to see Dr Roderick . . . you looked forward to him coming.'

Saturday was also the day Helen's mother, Patra, arrived from Greece for Helen's transplant. To Tim it was the occasion of some confusion: 'When we first met them, we thought Angeliki was Vasil's wife. He was middle-aged, and she was only sixteen, but she looked worn out with care. She looked as if she could easily have been his wife. She was expected to do the work in the room and look after her sister and be the donor. So when Patra arrived, we took her for Helen's grandmother. When we got to know Vasil better, he couldn't believe it. He roared with laughter.'

Tim went home the following day, and Sue was on her own again. She was still helping William to keep his diary, though the entries could only be repetitive:

> I was sick again after my morning tablets . . . I do not want anything to eat or drink. The doctor came and said I was doing fine . . . I was sick again after my afternoon tablets and had diarrhoea and then went to sleep at 7.30. I woke up for my mouthwash at 9.30 and watched football. [It was the World Cup.] I'm feeling homesick.

Then, on 9 June:

> I was sick again in the afternoon and had diarrhoea. Robert the teacher came to see me. Sister came and changed the lines on my drip. I forgot, I had nose and throat swabs etc., and a chest X-ray this morning . . . Helen had her transplant.

Helen's transplant was exactly a week after William's, on a Monday evening. Since Tim had gone home, Sue was sharing a room with Helen's mother, Patra. It was an impersonal place. A little less than eight feet square, it was set in the ward's central block, and therefore had no window – only an extractor fan for ventilation. The two narrow beds were covered in thin orange bedcovers, which did little to brighten the worn cream walls. For furniture, a single bedside cabinet stood in front of a metal locker, which in turn obstructed the view of the broken mirror on the wall. There were four coat-hooks. But the room was within twenty paces of Helen's and William's beds. For Patra and Sue, it was a kind of home.

'On the night of Helen's transplant,' Sue recalled later, 'Patra came into the room – in the dark. She smelt awful, but she crept into bed with all her clothes on. And of course she couldn't speak a word of English. I couldn't comfort her. I could hear her praying as she went to sleep . . . I felt so sorry for her. And then next morning Helen was quite bright; her mother came and hugged me, and her eyes sparkled, as though to say, "Thank God! – Helen was still all right".'

CHAPTER 17

Every time William was visited by one of the doctors, every time his temperature was taken, Sue and Tim asked themselves: has he picked up an infection? Every time the soles of William's feet and the palms of his hands were examined for signs of a rash, they had to face the possibility that the grafted marrow might itself be rejecting William. But beyond these immediate fears was the most important question of all: had the grafted marrow taken, had it been accepted by William's own tissue? If it had not, none of the other questions had any significance.

There was no alternative but to wait. In one sense the days seemed endless, with nothing but anticipation to fill them. In another, it was a struggle to get everything done in the time available. With the medical regime and domestic duties, Sue was busy.

'The second week after transplant, William was becoming much livelier. He would be awake by seven in the morning. About eight, we'd try to get him to have his mouthwash and his tablets – getting through them was an hour's job, because they made him feel so sick. I'd count out loud the sixty seconds he had to swill the mouthwash round, or William would check on his watch. Then the nurse would come in, with clean bedclothes in a plastic bin-bag which she'd sprayed with spirit. The clothes would have been picked out of the middle of a bundle, as soon as the linen trolley came into the ward, to keep them as sterile as possible. The scales would be brought in on a kind of wheel-chair, and they'd be sprayed. The nurse would get William off the bed and on to the scales to be weighed, and then to the armchair, so that we could strip the bed. The bed-frame, the mattress, the drip-stand and everything in the room had to be sprayed and wiped every day. So the bed was made, and William was ready to be washed in the chair – he never used the shower or the loo: it was too difficult to move the drip about; in any case all his urine bottles and bedpans had to be collected so the contents could be measured and tested. After all that, he couldn't get back on the bed quick enough. William liked to lie on the bed – that was where he felt best. Then at some time or other the floor had to be washed, and the windows and walls cleaned, and all the time you'd have a mask on and an apron and rubber gloves. Then Dr Roderick would come. In among all this, it was quite a job to fit yourself in a coffee and a piece of toast. William wasn't eating anything – and not drinking much, either. Everything he did drink had to be sterile.

'Quite often we had a visitor. Duffy often came. He was quite happy to chat to the nurses, sit in the little barrier-room and talk to Helen's father, Vasil. You never had to worry about him. Our visitors mostly came by the early-morning train from King's Lynn; if we didn't have a visitor, the first deadline was usually a teacher coming in about ten-thirty. William knew he had to be sick before Robert Milnes or Jane Horne came – he knew he would normally be sick within half an hour of his tablets going down; if he could keep them down for half an hour, they'd be doing their job. So he tried to get all that over first.'

Under the 1944 Education Act, every child in hospital has a right to education after they have been away from their own school for six weeks. But establishing the need for a permanent school within the Royal Free Hospital, and building it up, had taken many years. Now the average roll was about fifty children, scattered throughout the hospital. They included day-patients on kidney dialysis, and teenagers coming to the child psychiatry unit on a daily basis. Their ages ranged from three to nineteen; and though most of them could come to the school-room in Riddell Ward, some of the teaching had to be done elsewhere, one-to-one. Among the ten members of staff were a nursery nurse and a nursery teacher, and a number of specialists. Robert, the head teacher, taught science, but he was also a musician.

He found one piece of equipment, a keyboard, particularly useful. 'It can be sterilized, so I could take it into William's room. 'He was learning his Grade Four pieces at home, so I got them photocopied and we did quite a lot of work. I remember for the first few days his best friend was the vomit-bowl, but after that he was sitting up – I won't say he was desperate to work, but he enjoyed working. Sometimes, though, it's a terrible struggle. I've never found a child who didn't want to do some work – even if it was only making things. It's very important that children should be mentally occupied, because when they're not think-ing about their school work, they're going to be thinking about some-thing else. That can be damaging. A stay in hospital can put a young child back by up to a year. Sadly, the block can be the parents; if they decide the child is too ill to work – in other words, that school is a punishment which they can be let off – our job is much more difficult. It can take six months to win their confidence and get access.

'We're questioned quite a lot by parents about why we're here. "Can't we get away from you even here? Is nothing sacred? You come to hospital to be ill: have we got to put up with a teacher?" Sue and Tim weren't like that. Some parents spoil their children because they're in isolation – "You don't have to do your work today if you feel a bit grotty." For William, the same standards of discipline went on – and of politeness. Some children get terribly rude in isolation. I have also been asked: "What is the point of teaching dying children?" My answer is: "I don't see what right I have, or anybody else has, to deprive them of normality."'

Sue agrees: 'If Tim and I had known that William was dying, we'd still have wanted his life to be as normal as possible.'

Robert has a further argument. 'If I, as a teacher, can't be bothered to teach him, if I withdraw, aren't I giving the child a very clear message anyway that he is dying? I think that's very important. Provided the teaching is good, I think it's valuable, even if it's only for half a day.'

Jane Horne, who taught William geography, takes the same view. 'It's right that a child should think normal life goes on, despite problems. Once you start pulling out, children begin to say, "Gosh, there must be something really awful wrong with me." For that reason we go to intensive therapy, if someone's gone there with a major problem, because we want to keep the contact going – a major element of normality. After his transplant, William wasn't in that situation. He was remarkably good. He'd say, "I'm going to be sick"; he'd get rid of it all, and then say, "I'm fine now", and get on with his work. That was wonderful. He never felt sorry for himself.'

William's stay in hospital stimulated some new interests. In general, he did not enjoy geography, but when he realized that Eduardo came from Portugal and Helen came from Greece, suddenly the world opened up.

Jane Horne found that William also liked computers. 'We could do maths on the computer,' she says. 'It could be left with him, and he'd work on it through the hours of the night – twenty-five hours a day, William would have done. Children think they're playing games, but they're not. Snooker! Did William play snooker! You have a standard snooker table on the screen, and you have to guess the angles and type them in. The ball goes off at the precise angle you put in, and if you get it wrong, you don't pot the ball. William enjoyed that. He got very good at it.'

The computer could also be used to encourage creativity of a different sort. 'We had a program like Cluedo, the board-game. We wrote a story about how a microwave oven had been stolen from the Riddell Ward kitchen; and William had to interview the different suspects in their rooms, and give them things to say. The computer randomizes the results, and William had to be the hospital security officer and deduce who was the thief. It was great fun when one of the doctors went to gaol for stealing!'

William's isolation, and the particular characteristics of leukaemia, limited his activities. As the days went by, he had a good deal of nervous energy, for which Robert would have liked to have found an outlet. 'William was very lively in isolation,' he says, 'physically as well as mentally. That's unusual. He used to curl up and pretend to be asleep, and then hurl a ball at me. It's very difficult to think of anything you can use in sterile conditions to work off what's not so much energy – because they don't have much – but high spirits, exuberance. Some sort of punch-ball, perhaps. But you've got to be very careful. Leukaemic patients can bruise very easily. If they've got low platelets, you don't encourage them to hit things. The first suggestion was an exercise bike, but it didn't come while William was in hospital. But there can be a claustrophobic effect from isolation. Children just turn in on themselves – some children find it the most devastating experience.'

Everything William used had to be sterile – clay for modelling, books, even paper. Jane Horne found it limiting. Most equipment had to be new, and if, for instance, she needed to photocopy something for William, a clean sheet of paper had to be put underneath the photocopied sheet, and another above it, when she took it to him.

Sue had to keep the same rules. 'We'd buy a new ball for William. Every time it landed on the floor, we'd spray it again. He'd wear gloves to catch it. When William's post came, the envelopes never came into the room. The nurse would open the envelopes in the barrier-room. Then I'd poke my head round the door and, with gloves on, pull the letter out. Then I'd spray the letters – which made the ink run! And if he had a parcel, no brown paper was allowed into the room, no outer wrapping – just the new toy would go in.

'After a time, we used to go to the cupboard where the urine-bottles and the vomit-trays were kept, and get our own. We were always told to remove the top ones – they were in stacks – and take what we needed from the middle. Then each one had to be individually sprayed in the barrier-room before we took it in to William. We had to shut the door each time before passing the next one in. And we used to see Patra spraying her bare feet. She didn't wear shoes, just sandals.'

It was perhaps a weakness of the system that people with business in William's room did not all change out of their street shoes. But Malcolm Brenner was the first to agree that the reverse barrier nursing as practised by the Royal Free could not be perfect: 'The circumstances in which we had to do William's transplant, and other transplants at that time, were very unsatisfactory. The rooms weren't specially designed; they're ordinary side-wards. The degree of protection was fairly minimal, which is why almost all the patients got an infection.

'Over ten years ago, a specialized isolation ward was built which had filtered air, air-lock doors, and special individual bathrooms with sterilized water – that would really have cut infection down. But although funds were given to build it, the money was never allocated to run it. It didn't open; it was used for offices. Finally, though, we got the money from a variety of different charities, but it wasn't due to come into use till the autumn after William's transplant. It is open now.

'Our infection rate was very high, and our death rate from infection was high as well – ten per cent. That's about average, internationally, but higher than centres which have specialized units, which are coming into use round the world. They should have been established a long time ago; but they're quite expensive to run, because you need more nurses for individual rooms.'

William's progress was not marked by many obvious milestones. Eight days after his transplant, his diary records that when Sue came into his room, she found him on his feet for the first time:

> I got out of my covers, put my slippers on and walked to the TV and switched it on. That was my first step. I was on my own – it was about six-thirty in the morning. Everybody was quite pleased.

The next day Sister Jordan took the stitches out of the two wounds left by the insertion of the Hickman catheter.

Sister Jordan, once met, was not easily forgotten. She seemed to carry a breath of the outside world into the sterile world of the hospital. Years of experience – she was in her mid-thirties – had given her authority, but she had the knack of always treating patients and their families as people who had lives of their own. She could be strict, as William had noticed early on; the film crew on occasion drew her criticism for their invasion of William's room, even if it had been sanctioned by doctors. But most of the time, her professionalism had a down-to-earth, reassuring and, above all, human face. It was not difficult to imagine another Sister Jordan, off-duty, hair down; and indeed her figure was as familiar outside the hospital as in it, as she bicycled round the streets of Hampstead with the enthusiasm of a London-to-Brighton veteran.

Sue has a particular reason for remembering the occasion when Sister Jordan took out William's stitches: 'Sister Jordan said to William – joking, I thought – "If you're a good boy and let me take these stitches out, I'm going to take your mum for a cup of coffee." And she did. Afterwards, I was quite happy to come back to the hospital, but she said, "Do you fancy a drink? Shall we go to the wine bar? William will be all right. Don't worry." So I thought: Oh well, sister knows best. We walked back past the hospital, up to the village, to the wine bar; and lo and behold, it wasn't open. We had to wait. And it was two hours or so before we got back, and nothing had happened. William was all right. But I felt so bad – Duffy, Tim's brother, had been there a whole hour, and I'd been out drinking.'

Sister Jordan knew Sue felt guilty: 'Any mother would. But sometimes it gets to the point where you're sick of being in that room, with apron, mask and gloves. Your child's fed up with seeing you. There's nothing you can do about it except cross the days off on the calendar. But it wouldn't have helped us at all if Sue had got ill as well.'

Sue took other measures to relieve the pressure of hospital life. 'I used to keep a bottle of sherry in my room. And last thing at night, I always used to take a disposable cup and fill it half or three-quarters full – and I wouldn't sip it, I'd gulp it down. Then I'd lie down, and within a few minutes I'd be asleep. And if I didn't have it, because I'd run out, I missed it. That was the time I said my prayers, too. I never found the chapel at the Royal Free, though I used to go every day at Addenbrooke's, but I used to say my prayers at night.'

In the middle of the second week after William's transplant, a telephone was plugged into the socket which had earlier been installed in his room. That was an unusual privilege made possible by Julia McLaren's production assistant, Jane Whitworth. With the hospital's permission, she had circumvented the normal bureaucracy and, on the BBC's undertaking to meet the cost, persuaded British Telecom to act quickly.

William was once again in direct communication with his family. He found the telephone an antidote to home sickness. 'It was nice. I was a bit homesick sometimes. Grandma rang; and my aunties used to phone quite a bit, and friends. I used to ring before eight or after six, mostly — it was cheaper. I'd ring Grandma, perhaps in the morning, then perhaps she'd ring me in the afternoon. I phoned up the school once and spoke to some friends, and they phoned me once at dinner time.'

It was easier for William to keep in touch with home than with Helen in the room next door: 'She'd been lying in bed nearly all the time. She wasn't doing at all well. If I put my head far enough back against the window, I could just see her head on the pillow. But then she got a bit better and was starting to walk about. So I could see her when she felt like it, because if she came to her door, which had a window in it, I could stand and wave through my door. One day she wanted to see me, and I was on the bedpan. When I went to the door, she looked so much better from what she had been. But really you couldn't hear very much through the glass. I knew a few Greek words, "good morning", "good afternoon", and things. We got them all a Greek–English dictionary, and that helped. My dad and Helen's dad became good friends. They communicated with a sort of sign-language. Helen's dad used to look up in his book and find something in Greek and then point to the English; and my dad would say "brother" or something.'

CHAPTER 18

Tim spent the second week after William's transplant at home. Sue's mother would arrive about half past seven in the morning to help get the three younger children off to school. In the afternoon and evening, she would look after them and help put them to bed. Tim would work during the day, and usually spend the evenings on his own. He says that he learnt a lot about running his business while William was ill; he suddenly realized that he didn't need to be in the shop every day. Before that, it had been almost an addiction for Tim. He found that Claire was more than capable of running the business.

But if Claire was capable of managing the business in Tim's absence, she still found it worrying. She felt intimidated when the bank manager telephoned, for example, though she found that Tim was able to solve many problems at long-distance. 'I'd phone Tim, and he would say, "Well, there's money owing from so-and-so. Chase him up." And we always managed to placate the bank manager. It was lovely because sometimes, when I phoned Tim at the hospital, William would answer the phone. It was quite moving to hear him – he used to talk about his lessons.'

Money was never a real problem for Tim. 'In the first few days money came in from the family and close friends – food in the hospital, money for petrol, telephone change. In the end, in spite of all the travelling, the fuel bill for the car didn't seem to be any bigger than the year before – we weren't using the car every day to ferry the children around. Sue's mum and dad looked after the children and often paid for the week's shopping. They did the washing, so the tumbler wasn't going round and round. The electricity bill at home was so small that we reduced the standing order.

'We decided we wanted a computer of our own for William. I had two MGA sports cars I'd been doing up for years, at great cost. I was happy to sell them – and lose money on the deal. It really didn't matter. It provided money for the computer and a few other things.

'I managed to do some good deals, though. A friend went out and bought some gear one Saturday – three clocks and some bits and pieces. He rang Claire, and Claire rang me in London; was I interested, because he wanted cash to go out and buy another lot? I had a terrific deal really, sight unseen – but I knew the chap very well. So I picked the clocks up when I got home, and when I went back to London a week or so later I sold two of them on the way down, and some more odds and ends in London. Within three days I'd cleared my capital outlay, which left me with one very nice clock to stand in the shop, with no capital tag on it. I made quite a few contacts in London. I used to wander round the antique shops whenever I got a break from the hospital.'

In the middle of the second week after William's transplant, Tim came back to London, meaning to allow Sue to go home for a break. But he developed a cold and could not risk infecting William. He had to go back to Norfolk, where it took him more than a week to recover. As a result Sue missed one of the events in the village calendar, the school sports day. The sports were held in the playing-field opposite the school. The sun shone, the bunting was out, tea was laid on trestle tables. All the children took part, watched by Tim, Neville, Jean and other members of the family. Edward could only manage to complete the egg-and-spoon race – to loud applause – with his thumb held firmly over the egg and the spoon upside down. The occasion was a moment of normality.

The following Monday, some of William's school-friends compiled an account of the sports on the school tape recorder – mainly lists of results, emphasizing the triumphs of the speaker. Mrs Appleby acted as organizer. 'We recorded assembly, too – William asked us to, so we sent it off to him. And we sent him some marvellous jokes . . . knock-knock, that sort of thing. They were funny in their unfunniness, if you know what I mean. William sent us some tapes back. He played his exam piece on his keyboard. He switched it on, and said: "I'm going to do so-and-so – hang on." And the children all laughed. And he spoke a few Greek words – *kali mera*, good-morning, and how are you? And he told them he had a Greek girl next to him – that was Helen.

'We also sent him a big poster from school with "Hello, William" on it. Sue said he always wanted it on the wall by his bed, so that he could read the names. He would often roll over in bed and look at them – and he worked out whose names weren't there, because they were away from school. You couldn't do that with a big school, could you? Kay, Mick, Kieran and Thomas – they all wrote fairly big, because it was their idea, and then people's writing got smaller and smaller towards the bottom. And the funny thing was, Naomi wrote her name in full: Naomi Clayton . . . in the tiniest writing.'

A fortnight after transplant, William had his regular chest X-ray. For Sue, the portable X-ray machine had unpleasant associations. She remembered how, in Addenbrooke's, the sudden need for an X-ray could signal a problem of some kind. She did not immediately realize that, this time, it was simply a routine check for possible lung infections.

The following day Dr Brenner planned to take a sample of William's grafted bone-marrow to see if it was growing. Already he had been taking regular blood samples.

'We took them three or four times a week, to make sure William's metabolism was OK, that he wasn't losing any important minerals, that his liver wasn't inflamed. In William it was fine. He was having a very uncomplicated post-transplant course. About a third of patients do, a third have complications like infection, and a third have a very bad time of it . . . severe infections, or bleeding, or "graft versus host" disease.

'The first signs of the transplant taking usually occur in the blood in the veins. As soon as white cells, neutrophils and lymphocytes, reappear in the blood, that's a sign of engraftment. But we have to do a marrow test to make sure they are really from the marrow, not transferred from outside in some way by transfusion – because the numbers are very low, perhaps a tenth or a twentieth of what they would be in a normal person. Sometimes the blood shows white cells very quickly and the marrow just confirms it. Even though it's one per cent of one per cent of the donor's marrow, it can start production very quickly. Sometimes, though, you don't see anything in the circulation, but when you look at the marrow you see primitive cells there. They've started, but they haven't yet come out into the bloodstream.'

Sue knew about the bone-marrow test some time in advance. 'The film crew were coming in that day. It was all planned. And that morning, Tuesday, Dr Brenner came into the little lobby, and said to me, "I'm sure everything will be all right – the blood count is doing the right things, but we'll do the bone-marrow tests and let you have the results later today."

'About ten in the morning, Dr Simons came in with a cylinder on a trolley to put William to sleep. There was an injection, and then a mask And their casual manner! Dr Simons would just sit there talking about what he'd be having for lunch; he'd be twiddling knobs here and turning knobs there, and then he'd just lift William's chin up, and put something in his mouth. He knows his job inside out – I felt completely confident with him. But he was chatting away, and there was my child under an anaesthetic.

'That was the first time I stayed in the room for an operation. It was only a needle going into the back of William's pelvis. If there'd been any actual blood involved, I don't think I could have been there. As it was, I stayed over on the other side of the room. The thing I didn't like was seeing William sitting there one minute, talking and the next minute under an anaesthetic, just gone. You roll him over, and everything goes flop. You imagine that's what he'd look like if he died . . . pale, ill, so lifeless. But it was over very quickly.

'William came round in half an hour or so. That was the day he started eating peanuts. Julia filmed him. It was the first food he'd had in his mouth since the day after he was admitted. He soon brought them back up – but the pleasure of just seeing him eating them!

'Tim phoned in the middle of the day to see how we'd got on with the tests. But I didn't tell him what Dr Brenner had said in the morning. I saved that, because I'd been told the results would come later on in the day, and I thought there was no point in building up hopes . . .

'About five-thirty Dr Brenner came and told William and me that the graft had taken; and that in a few days' time – possibly a week or ten days (remember this was only a fortnight after transplant) – we could go home. I just couldn't believe it. His blood count had to get up to one, and it was about 0.4 at this stage, but once it got up to one, we were away.

'Then he told us what would happen when we went home, and he gave us a leaflet about hygiene and food and so on. So I phoned Tim – Julia had arranged to film the call. Tim wasn't expecting the results – I know some patients have to wait longer – but part of the speed was due to the fact that the film crew were there.

'When I told Tim we'd got the results, he said, "Oh, I wanted to be there for them . . ." He didn't know the film crew were in William's room, so I said – I'm not quite sure what I said, but I ignored Tim and carried on. He didn't realize that I was being filmed there and then.

'And then William came on the phone and talked to Harriet. He just said "Thank you", very politely but solemnly; and it sounded as if she said at the other end, "What for?" And he said, "It's taken." And again it sounded as if she said, "What's taken?" And he said, "We think your bone-marrow's taken." Then William actually said to Tim,

"Dad, you know I might be home in ten days; well, don't tell the others . . . because I might not be." And I didn't, and nor did Tim.'

'No. I'm sure I would have told Claire, and Grandma and Grandad – anyone at home who needed to know, but I didn't tell the other children. William didn't want to build them up. After the waiting it was something of an anticlimax to be told the news over the phone. I had hoped to be there to share in the excitement. But I remember that night. I had an appointment over at Boston – and that was the worst deal I've ever had. I bought such rubbish: I still can't get shot of it. I've got a lot of it left . . .'

CHAPTER 19

Almost three months had passed since William's leukaemia had first been diagnosed. In Terrington St John, the three younger children had had time to adjust to their new way of life. And so had Sue's parents, Jean and Neville.

Neville felt the burden of added responsibility. 'Whether the children were playing in the village, on the crossroads – that was our problem. We never went far from the house. There's a lot of difference between not going anywhere when you've got a choice to go or not to go, and when you haven't. But it didn't really change us. Jean never had to miss having her hair done on Saturday. But it wasn't a new thing, having to worry. It wasn't so long since we'd been worrying about Susan's sister, when she was ill.'

To Sue, it became clear that however well the children knew their grandparents, living with them would bring change. Although life seemed to go on in much the same way, there were differences – as Naomi clearly perceived.

'Grandma usually gets up about six. She makes quite a rattle with the kettle, so you wake up. Grandad always leaves his tea-things out from the night before, because he goes to bed later than Grandma, so they have to be washed up and put away by Grandma.

'Life at Grandma's wasn't the same at all. It was strange, but it was OK. We pretended it was normal. We had to pretend very hard. When we went over to Grandma's house, I used to take things with me – books and nighties and a dressing-gown. What I pretended to do was bring the whole house. I put some things in a case, and I had a little house and I put that in too, as if I'd brought the whole house.

'I missed William, and Mum and Dad. Some of the time I was miserable – not all of the time. I would want to go and be miserable – but I wouldn't when I was with Grandma and Grandad. There wasn't much to cry about. Mum and Dad came home – we saw them quite often. But I did cry sometimes by myself.

'We knew we were visitors. We were on our best behaviour. Why we don't use our best behaviour all the time is what I want to know! The food was different. Grandma likes cooking carrots, which I don't like.

Mum doesn't usually give them to me, or she only gives me about three. Grandma gives me about ten. You have to eat them, even if you get cabbage as well. And if we didn't, we'd get Grandad's big slipper. I didn't get it, but it was under Grandad's writing-bureau. Grandma and Grandad are quite strict. They did get cross with us, but not very, very, very cross. Not as cross as they can get. Then they'd tap us, but they wouldn't smack us.

'We didn't usually go around people's houses. We weren't allowed out of the house after six o'clock. And we didn't have time to go out before – having a wash after school, having tea. Edward went to bed at seven; we went to bed at eight-thirty.

'There was one strict rule. We were not allowed to pick up the phone, unless we were told to. William rang *us* up, and we only got about two minutes' chat with him because we didn't want to use too much electricity.

'School was OK. I prefer the holidays, though. I find maths is easy. English is not all that good. Every Sunday we went to church. We have Sunday School through half of it; there, you just learn about the Bible, doing the story of Elijah in pictures. It's quite hard – but it's not too dreadful.

'We usually think of Dad as the head of the family, and William as head of the children. I wasn't used to being head of the children. It didn't work out very well. I didn't say much in the first few days of thinking it . . . because I was wondering how William was getting on and things. It's quite hard to be head of the family, and be bossy. Harriet and Edward are difficult to control.

'We used to play in the barn. It was fun to take off our shoes and socks and clamber up the corn and barley. We dig up corn, and we get two big stones, and then we make flour.

'Indoors, Grandma was usually in a different room, unless it was our help-day. We invented some new games. Grandad and Grandma had lots of games we hadn't played. We don't do them any more because they're old-fashioned. And Grandma's still got lots of children's clothes. I tried on Auntie Carolyn's best Sunday dress, and Mummy's little party dress. That's small, and it's blues and purples . . . just above the knee. It's got about six petticoats underneath which make it stand out. Grandma's got lots of curtains, which we used for cloaks. We did plays with titles like "The Bossy Princess". We did the first play after Christmas – before William was ill. It wasn't all that good, only about five minutes. There was this unhappy princess, and she had to find a boy in two weeks. So she put an advert in the paper. She found a boy, but he was ugly. Harriet was the princess. I was the mother, and Edward was the ugly prince.'

Harriet occasionally let her feelings show, even to outsiders. On one occasion the three children visited Rosemary Wood and her family.

'Harriet went completely over the top,' Rosemary recalls. 'That wasn't normal. She went berserk, and screamed and kicked. I just gathered her up and held her on my knee and hugged her really tight for about twenty minutes; and she just sobbed and sobbed, and then she was all right. I had them all from ten till six – and it rained. Six children and rain.'

The same thing happened on one of Sue's visits home: 'I was taking Harriet to school, and she screamed. She really screamed. Mrs Appleby took her from me. She could see that it was upsetting me to cope with her screaming and crying. So I went back home on my own. And Mrs Appleby phoned: Harriet was fine the minute I'd gone – no problem at all.'

Edward was only four. He, too, sometimes cried. Jean and Neville used to take him into their bed, as Neville remembers: 'I said to him, "Don't you wet the bed tonight, Edward. I don't want you weeing on me." And he whispered, "I won't, Grandad. I'm facing Grandma."'

Mrs Appleby, Edward's teacher, was very fond of him: 'If I wasn't,' she says, 'he'd be dead by now, or he'd have been moved to another school. You can't be cross with him for any length of time, because he just grins at you. But I've sussed out the charm. All four of them have it . . . they walk in – a lot of children just look at you – but they walk in and beam at you.

'Edward was very young when he started school; only four and a half. Had it been anyone else, and the circumstances normal, I would have asked Sue to take him away. He wasn't ready. But I felt very strongly that Grandma and I were the two anchors in his life. When William went away, Edward had to have his chair and his desk as close to me as it was possible to get, so that he could literally touch me. And at assembly, I always had to be there with my arm round him, or have him on my lap.

'All four of Sue's children are extremely bright. And William and Harriet use that brightness. Naomi and Edward are extremely hard work to get anything out of. It's just that they can't be bothered. Naomi says, "If I do my sums, I just get more." With Edward, I can literally spend all day trying to get work out of him. Start in the morning with simple addition, and still be at it at a quarter past three in the afternoon. He digs his heels in – you can keep him in at lunch and get really cross with him, and he'll take all day, shouting out how long each sum is taking him. I'm not the sort of person that will let children win. I feel that if I let them win at this stage, then my life will be a misery later on. And there comes a time when they've got to work all day.

'Edward's an enigma, and so is Naomi, I think.'

Sue sometimes finds Naomi difficult, too: 'If you tell her to say "Thank you", she'll say "Thank you", but you know she doesn't really mean it. Or goodbye. You say "Say 'Goodbye' nicely" . . . and she'll say "Goodbye nicely" – and stare you out.

'Naomi's far less feminine than Harriet, even though Harriet's younger. Naomi's the mothering kind. If you go anywhere with young children, Naomi's the one with her arm round the little ones. She'd make a good nurse. She doesn't care about clothes at all. She's inclined to look at jumble and say, "Oh, isn't that chiffon scarf lovely, Mummy?" Anything threaded with lurex, or sequins, or a bit of fur, attracts her. She'd wear all the colours of the rainbow. Harriet's getting beyond wanting her clothes from Mothercare and M. & S. You have to go to Tammy Girl and get bangles and beads and headbands, and all the fashion things.

'Naomi and Edward live in a little world of their own. William and Harriet need friends; and they have to have older friends. They like to be in favour with older children. And they're tidier. Both William and Harriet will have a toy, and put it back in its box. In some ways they'd rather not play with it and spoil it. With Naomi and Edward, the box will be broken and a piece lost, and they're not bothered. They've played with it, they've done various things with it. And then they find something new to do with the pieces that are left.'

Friends and relations did their best to lighten the load on Jean and Neville by taking the children out for the day. In Neville's view, it didn't always work out for the best.

'It was more trouble, we thought, to send them away for the day than it was to keep them. You've got to bear in mind that people took them for a day each to look after them . . . and they could have a day of peace or a day of trouble. And they chose the day of peace. The last thing in the world they want to do is upset the children. So they gave them a good time . . . and to some extent they spoiled them. David and Jo did spoil them.'

David and Jo had been engaged for some time. In principle, they were favourably disposed towards children. One day they decided on an expedition to the north Norfolk coast, to Hunstanton. They all went on the beach, and the children caught shrimps. Then Duffy thought it was time for some food.

'We got to the restaurant, and the girls decided they wanted to powder their noses. So off they go, and I'm left with Edward. And Edward says, "I'd like to go as well, Uncle Duff." "Fair enough, Edward" . . . so off we go. Very inexperienced with children, I am, being a bachelor. And he said, "Do a big job, Uncle Duff." Fair enough, again. I managed to understand that. So before I could say, "Do you want a hand?", trousers were down and he'd jumped on the toilet. I didn't know what to do really, so I said, "Do I wipe your bottom, Edward?" "Oh yes, you wipe my bottom." And he bent down so that his head was literally touching the ground, so I could get at him.

'With that done, we go back upstairs to meet the girls. Naomi's feeling sick, but we have our fish and chips, and everybody's got a drink, and we're quite happy. But Edward decides he's got another big job to do. And I said, "No, Edward, you can't. You can't – you've only just been." We were on banquette seating, and he climbed over me and over Jo, and stood in the aisle of the restaurant, marching on the spot and swinging his arms and saying, "I want to go, I want to go, and do a *big job*." And he's got a very determined way, and a very deep voice. So we go again, and he's sitting there – I'd got the door ajar, so I could keep an eye on him. And people were coming in, and the fumes were drifting, and all of a sudden he says, "That was loud, wasn't it, Uncle Duff?" Extraordinary, to say the least. But Edward wasn't perturbed at all.

'We all got in the car to come home. Naomi was still feeling sick. She thought the meal was quite expensive, so she'd better eat it all up. We stopped twice, and then with about seven miles to go, I decided we'd have to stop again. I held Naomi's head. Harriet wanted to go to the loo. She got behind a barrel in the lay-by and Jo had to stand in front and not look. Edward, believe it or not, was sitting in the front of the car, with his knees up and his hands over his face, shouting, "Shut the door, shut the door. I don't want to hear you being sick." But nothing happened. Then, when we finally got home Naomi got out of the car and was sick by the gate. I don't think Grandad was too pleased.'

Neville was annoyed. 'David said, "Naomi's just been sick." I said, "That doesn't matter." "Good job it wasn't in my car," he said. I ought to have told him, "It's a pity it wasn't – next time you take them out, you keep control." Those children had more to eat in a day than they should have had in a week.'

CHAPTER 20

◆

At the Royal Free Hospital, Sue and Tim were settling into a routine. One would go home for three or four days, while the other looked after William. At the changeover, they would spend one or two nights in London together.

Sue and Tim depended on each other. William's illness had brought them closer. But whether the growing hope that William might be cured loosened their self-control, or whether the relentless pressure of anxiety proved too much, there was one occasion – and only one, they say – when feelings got the better of them. It was late. Having settled William for the night, Sue was in the barrier-room, chatting to the staff nurse. She often found it helpful and reassuring to hear from the medical staff that William was doing well. 'All of a sudden,' she says, 'Tim stormed in. I felt so embarrassed – he just lost his rag.'

Tim says he only asked if Sue was coming to bed. 'I'd been in bed for half an hour, waiting for Sue. I was desperately tired, and I knew that if I went to bed and to sleep on my own, Sue would come in and wake me up. So I went off to find where she was.'

'Well,' says Sue, 'he certainly made his feelings clear. And I said to the nurse, "Oh, dear, what's hit us? I think I'd better go." I can remember being cross with Tim when I got to our room, for causing a scene. I didn't feel sorry that I'd kept him waiting twenty minutes. I was angry that he'd lost his temper. And for the next hour, we had words. But it was only tension. The nurse fully understood. Next day Tim went back and apologized.'

'Really it was just tiredness. I was absolutely shattered. Sue was shattered too, but she'd got somebody to talk to.'

Like Sue, Tim found plenty to do in looking after William. But other jobs caught his attention, too. He noticed that one of the ward showers was not working. Instead of reporting the fault, Tim bought the missing part and repaired the shower himself. No one complained. But he ran into trouble in the ward kitchen.

'The stove was dirty, really dirty. So I gave it a good going over. The cleaner whose job it was to do it was most upset. There was quite a row, and I had to pacify her. You could understand it really, I suppose – it was her job under threat. Afterwards she always used to make a big joke of it – "Good morning, Mr Clayton – nice clean stove today!"'

William's condition was improving. The last of his hair had fallen out; his tablets and mouthwashes still made him sick; five or six times a day he would announce 'I think I've had an accident', and his underpants would have to be changed – diarrhoea was something the doctors watched carefully. But in himself William was feeling brighter. He was less demanding. He even realized the need for Sue to get away from the hospital from time to time. Sue was grateful.

'William was too good to be true. He was so thoughtful. He'd tell you to go and have your breakfast. But he also enjoyed being on his own. He'd often say: "I feel tired now – do you want to go down to the shops?" I'd switch off the TV, leave him a stack of urine-bottles and vomit-trays, and go. He'd sleep; and if sleep didn't come, he'd ask the nurse to crank his bed up – he couldn't do that for himself – and turn the TV on. Or he'd be on the phone. On one occasion his buzzer slipped off the bed after I'd gone, so he decided to have some fun. He phoned the hospital and asked for Riddell Ward. He looked through the barrier-room window towards the ward desk and saw Charge Nurse David pick up the phone. "Hello, David. This is William. I've dropped my buzzer – could someone come and pick it up in case I need anything?" David looked across and smiled and waved. He was amused. It was lovely to see that spark of life.'

Some parents were much more reluctant to leave their children. Little Eduardo Cunha, who was now three rooms away from William, was in the middle of his second block of chemotherapy – a more prolonged treatment than William's had been. His father, big Eduardo, was still in Portugal. His mother, Fernanda, was on her own. It worried Sister Jordan.

'Fernanda never left Eduardo. Children are very adaptable. As long as there was someone there with him, it didn't really matter for an hour or two if she wasn't there. Yet it was so important for her, because every day there was worry; and she was in that room, or near Eduardo, every day. And she had the added disadvantage of being from a foreign country, and not speaking English. One mum from Turkey fainted when we put in a Hickman catheter: you're from Turkey, you're in England, and we're doing all these horrible things to your child. Sue and I did take Fernanda out for a drink one night. We sat outside the George, didn't we, and had two glasses of wine.'

'I think we actually had three,' said Sue. 'Fernanda got quite giggly. She'd never had three glasses of wine before. She relaxed, she smiled, she talked about big Eduardo.'

Helen's mother, Patra, had difficulties, too, in understanding the hospital staff or anybody else. Like Sue, Tim did his best. 'We learnt to communicate – by signs, or in any way we could. Vasil and Patra and Sue and I could hold a very disjointed conversation. We had lots of fun trying – if you could call it fun.

'Similar problems produced a bond, strong and close. I remember going for a walk with Vasil on Hampstead Heath. He saw a TV in a skip – it would have been worth two hundred pounds to him in Greece. He was a very canny dealer. He would have had the coat off your back. We had marvellous times, in short bursts. When Patra discovered a new word, or what we meant by something – the way she would brighten up then, like a ray of sunshine!'

At any one time, there might be half a dozen or more families in Riddell Ward, anxiously awaiting the outcome of treatment on their children, often bone-marrow transplants. Though beds were provided for everyone, parents would often sit up in the common-room, for all its bleakness, into the small hours of the morning, discussing their shared problems.

A week or two after the news that William had accepted his transplant, Eduardo Cunha came back to Britain from Portugal. The authorities had finally agreed to fund little Eduardo's treatment. Big Eduardo was very conscious that he and Fernanda were in a foreign country.

'We felt really, really alone. But when we were in the hospital we met Sue and Tim, and more parents with leukaemia children; and when the same problem is shared, it's less.

'Me and my wife, we came here two years before, because we won a prize and they paid the flight and the hotel for one week. So we knew the usual things about London; and since I came to the hospital, I have learnt very well all the corridors of the hospital. If they say, "You go to test on eleventh floor", we know where it is.

'But London was very strange, because I live in a small town, and I prefer that. Sometimes I need to go to Lisbon for work. In the evening, I come back to my home. And if I have to stay two or three days, I work late; then I go to the hotel. But London, for me, is a very strange city. The first time I came here, I said, "Where are the English people?" Everybody spoke English here, OK, but I didn't find the traditional English people I was expecting.

'I understand in a sense the way people react here, because there are so many problems. They can't trust anybody. I understand why, if I ask a young girl, seventeen or eighteen, "Excuse me, can you tell me . . .", she doesn't look, she goes on walking. She doesn't trust me. But the first time, I couldn't understand, I felt angry, and I said, "You react in that way, you are really English." But that's not fair, because I met lots of wonderful English people. We had English people in our factory, and they were from Manchester. Some of them didn't like London. But some English people, for me, are cold people, calculating people. Some parents I met in the hospital, it seems they are expecting to get their children out of the house, when they are grown-up, because the parents want to have their own life. I think in a different way.

'And another example. One day a lady came into the parents' room and said, "Oh, very clean room!" I said, "Yes, I cleaned everything, ashtrays, tables, chairs, sink." She said, "Are you mad? That's a cleaner's job." "But I live here. I like to live in a clean place." "That's not a reason," she said. My God – how to think! But then at other times I saw English ladies doing the same as I did. Probably that lady was an exception.'

Apart from the comfort families got from each other and from the nurses, the services provided by the school often included more than conventional education. Sue could not go into Helen's room to visit her, but she was able to watch what the teachers did. 'One teacher could speak Greek. She would take books and tapes in to Helen, music and tapes in Greek. They would make mobiles, and they would write home. She'd get Helen to write to her brothers and sisters, do drawings. Helen couldn't speak English – and no way was she going to try. She wasn't interested. But she looked forward to the tapes. The school did everything they could to encourage her, even if it was only holding her hand and reading her a story.'

Robert Milnes has often had experience of doing more than merely teaching. On one occasion he visited a fifteen-year-old in an adult surgical ward.

'It came out that he'd had an appendectomy – he'd learnt that word. But he didn't know what his appendix was. So for two days this boy – who was behaving as though he was about thirteen, because often children regress when they come into hospital, in behaviour and temperament – was quite worried, because he didn't know how he was going to get on without his appendix, but he didn't like to make a fuss. Two days is a long time for thoughts like that to be going round anybody's head. Well, I have a kit showing the digestive system, which you cut out and colour. So I could reassure him. You can often discover something that's causing children distress at school, too, which they haven't admitted. This boy couldn't do number bases – so he went back to his school a world authority on number bases.

'We sometimes re-route children who have left school because they didn't like it, and who have begun the downward path to ruin ... smashed up on a motorbike or something. By the time they've lain there for three months they've re-thought their lives, and you can arrange for careers or college and so on. It's the kids who can't read who find all the derelict buildings and fall through the floors and break their legs.

'Teachers are also used in a diagnostic role. For instance, we always expect Septemberitis at the beginning of the school year ... the first year into secondary school, or the first year at exams. A child might come in with acute back-ache ... can't stand up. A teacher can be useful in finding out if something's wrong at school ... or at home – parents who expect too much, say. Then you do something about the underlying cause, and the back-ache goes. I've known a case get as far as operating before the real cause was found.

'In a place like Riddell Ward, a lot of things come out in written work. Something crops up, and a child wants to ask questions: is it dangerous, what I've got? William knew he might die. He told me. But a lot of parents don't want their children to know. I've known a situation – not at the Royal Free – where a child was as nasty as she could possibly be because she knew what she'd got could kill her. The parents didn't want her to know; and the child decided that the best way of avoiding mother and father missing her would be to behave as badly as possible. In effect, they'd be glad that she was dead. She went on behaving badly till she died.'

Towards the end of June, William was doing so well that Sue and Tim thought they could give Naomi a treat. It was arranged that Tim would bring her down to London for the weekend. Sister Jordan gave her a room to herself, one of the leukaemia isolation rooms down the corridor from the ward. To Naomi's excitement, it had its own bathroom, like a hotel.

Sue and Tim decided to take her out for something to eat. Sue suggested a pizza. 'We went to the Pizza Hut and got a take-away; and then we went down to the little square at the bottom of the hill below the hospital, to eat it. Near the shops, where the roads meet at the lower end of Hampstead Heath, there's a little triangle of grass with a monument or a drinking fountain in the middle of it. It was new to Naomi, and exciting for her, just being in London.'

There was more pizza than they could eat. Tim noticed a tramp sitting on a bench nearby. 'I thought he might just fancy a bit of pizza; and, like a fool, I asked him. He went absolutely bananas. He swore and cursed, and threw it at me, and kicked it.'

Tim apologized to the tramp if he had offended him; but Sue could see that that would not be the end of the matter. 'He was really coming after Tim, and his language was a bit thick – he was effing and blinding – and I thought: this isn't for Naomi to hear; so I moved away with her.'

Tim walked off in the opposite direction. 'I wanted him to follow me, and leave Sue and Naomi alone. I was thinking: I'm going to have to lay one on this bloke, just to quieten him down. What a situation – you offer a man a bit of pizza and you end up poking him in the nose! Naomi was quite shaken by it. That was her first experience of London.'

Next morning, Sue, Tim and Naomi drove to Ealing for a barbecue with some friends. When they picked up the car in the hospital car park, they found one of the rear windows smashed. Surprisingly, nothing had been taken from the cardboard boxes inside, which were filled with clocks and antiques which Tim hoped to sell. But Naomi was shocked at the vandalism. Or was it, she asked, the tramp's revenge?

Overall, however, Sue felt the weekend had been good for Naomi. 'The nurses looked after her and made her feel special, and convinced her they were taking good care of her brother. On the Sunday morning, Tim and I relaxed a bit. We didn't get up till half past seven, a quarter to eight – we were usually up soon after six, and William often was, too. I put my dressing-gown on and went to see what Naomi was doing. She wasn't in her room, so I went to look for her. I walked past William's corner – I could just see him in bed – so I waved to him, and went on looking. I couldn't find her, so I went into the barrier-room outside William's room, to see if she was there – and I looked through the window, and there sat Naomi, playing cards.'

'I got up in the morning,' explained Naomi, 'and went to Mum and Dad's room – but they were asleep. So I went back, and Sister Daniels asked me to take William's tablets in. I had to put on a mask, an apron and gloves. What the nurse did with the gloves – she filled them with water, tied knots in the end, put them together and pretended they were a ten-legged spider – they were bulging with water. I put the tablets down by William's bed, and all of a sudden William woke up. And he asked me, "Would you stay for a game of cards?" So I was there for hours, until Mum came.'

Sister Jordan might not have approved of relaxing the rules of isolation. But William appreciated his first visit from the outside world.

During Naomi's visit Tim bought some Kentucky fried chicken to eat in the hospital. He put one portion into the microwave for William – but William could only eat a mouthful. Sue did not expect much more. 'He might have a round of toast for breakfast, one fish finger for lunch. He'd open a packet of crisps – he'd have four or five. The doctor said if it was crisps and sweets, that was better than nothing. And he was having to drink about a litre a day – fizzy lemonade, always out of a fresh bottle. Because before William could go home, he had to show some sign that his eating and drinking were at least beginning to return to normal. So that became another chore.

'Quite soon after the bone-marrow test which showed the graft had taken, they cut his drip feed to half – not gradually but dramatically, one day full feed, the next day half. So all the time you were pushing him to eat and drink and take the tablets. It was a perpetual struggle, and just as you thought you were winning, you'd relax – with the fluid, say; and the chart would show impurities in his urine, and you'd have to get him to drink more. And all the time on half drip feed, he was losing weight.

'The other thing we were watching was William's blood count. When the bone-marrow test was done, it was 0.4. It had to get to 1.0 before he could go home. That might be a week or ten days. And three weeks later, there we were, still waiting.'

Dr Brenner did not seem worried. 'I don't know why it happens. It often does . . . I guess because you've damaged the normal environment of the marrow by everything you've done. And though you can get a little bit of production from what's left, in order to get full production the marrow has to repair itself generally – which is a much slower process. It's very common: you get an initial rise in the blood count, then a plateau, and then a rise again.'

Nor was Sue worried by the delay, until a second bone-marrow test was done. 'They'd said William wouldn't have another one before he went home. When I heard that they were going to do a test after all, I had this feeling there must be something wrong. But they told me not to worry. They were just having another look, now that four weeks had gone by. And his blood count was up a bit, 0.5 or 0.6.'

In the room next to William's, Helen was following the same course as he was, but a week behind him. For her, the treatment never seemed to go as smoothly. William had seen Helen walk into her room with long, dark hair. Now it had been cut short and was falling out. She looked old and fragile. Temperamentally she was a bad patient. She hated her parents or the nurses to touch her. She used to scream and shout when her bed was made. But the graft from her sister, Angeliki, had taken; and three weeks after her transplant Helen was well enough for the hospital to allow her mother to go home to Greece. The other five children in the family could not be abandoned any longer.

Sue and Tim continued to take turns looking after William and spending time at home. Having missed the school sports day, Sue was pleased to be able to take the children to the church summer fair. 'It was my sister Jane's birthday. It was nice to come home and actually go to something in the village with the children. It was the sort of thing that children love – with a bran-tub, and coming home with a bag full of bits and pieces. Then I went back to the Royal Free the next day. It was a very quick visit home; but I knew that hopefully we were coming to the end of our spell in hospital. I was confident that William was coming home – not that it was all over, but that things were going a lot better than we'd anticipated. They were going as planned.'

At the beginning of July, William's blood count reached the magic figure: one. Visitors were allowed into his room – two at a time, and without masks. On Monday, 7 July, almost six weeks after William was admitted to the Royal Free Hospital, Sue and Tim were told that if the blood count next day was still good, they could go home.

In the middle of the morning, Dr Roderick brought them their release. 'The blood counts, the different elements, had come up sufficiently for us to think he would be safe. The platelets count was good enough to stop him having a nasty bleed if he banged himself. And the white count would be enough to prevent serious bacterial infection. That's not to say he couldn't get any infections, particularly from viruses or fungi. But we thought he would be safe against violent infections which cause a collapse of the blood pressure. There are certain strains of bacteria which you're susceptible to when your blood count's very low, which can give you very acute shock within hours. If you're not treated, you can die. So we try to avoid sending people home for two or three weeks so that they're safe from these overwhelming attacks.'

'It took us nearly all day to pack,' Sue remembers. 'We had to get the medication together and we waited for ages at the pharmacy for prescriptions. Tim had already taken some things home, but we'd been accumulating clothes and presents for weeks. In any case, once you'd been told to go, you never went quickly. You never thought: I'm free – let's go. You took your time. We certainly didn't sit with our bags packed, waiting to be told we could go. We knew we were going into the big, wide world, full of disease and danger.'

CHAPTER 21

It was not a triumphant homecoming for William. None of the other children could even be in the house to greet him. The previous weekend Harriet had stayed with a friend who later went down with shingles, so she was potentially infectious. Naomi was also a possible source of danger: it turned out that one of the children she had met during her weekend at the Royal Free Hospital had been in contact with chicken-pox. Finally, on Sue's last visit home the family had been visited by children who later developed measles. So Naomi, Harriet and Edward were all quarantined at their grandmother's house.

Tim and Sue's house was thoroughly aired. There was nothing else Sue could do.

'You just had to keep your fingers crossed. It was pointless saying anything to anybody about the contacts. They couldn't be helped. We were lucky to know about them. But the children couldn't mix with William at all. But there was a big "Welcome Home" poster on the door – which the three children had made with Grandma and Grandad, with tinsel round it. Mum was so ashamed because there was a spelling mistake – "Wellcome"! William appreciated being home. Everything looks better when you've been away. I can remember him going to his room and just being pleased to see it.'

It was seven o'clock by the time Sue got William into the house. She felt their routine had been completely disrupted, and in fact it took several days for her and Tim to adjust to looking after William them-selves. For medication they matched the hospital's timetable, but otherwise they treated him as though he was well. Though he got up late, he did not stay in bed. The consequence was that whereas in hospital everything they needed was in one small room, at home, they had to keep a box containing mouthwashes, lozenges, tissue-box, vomit-tray, which could be carried round the house. All William's food had to be cooked.

There was one extra piece of bodily housekeeping Sue had to attend to. 'William's Hickman catheter had to be kept liquid so that the blood didn't clot in it. The Hickman has a screw cap to keep it closed. Every two or three days I had to clamp it, unscrew the cap and screw on a syringe of special fluid, unclamp it again, inject the fluid and thereby flush the catheter. Then I would clamp it up again and screw the cap on. If I'd left it open, the heart would have sucked in air as it beat. Malcolm Brenner compared the effect with having air in your brakes – it would have made the system go spongy and prevented the heart pumping blood efficiently. William always used to have the clamps with him. When he went to bed, he'd have them in his pyjama pocket, just in case something happened.

'After a day or two, he was able to go into the garden. The other children would come round. Grandma would bring them in the car, and when they arrived all the windows would have to be kept closed. It was scorching hot weather – they'd be absolutely cooking – but they could see William and he could show them things.'

Sue's mother was shocked by William's appearance. 'We didn't think he'd ever be the same as he was before. We didn't think he'd get rid of the scorch from the radiation. He'd got an old man's skin, hadn't he? All his neck was mottled, like grimed-in dirt, brown and rusty.'

Sue knew that it wasn't only William's neck that was affected. 'When I washed him, it was like that under his arms and round his groin. It flaked off, and peeled off. Mind you, we were happy to accept him like that. It wasn't the end of the world.

'Our next appointment with anyone wasn't until the end of the week. We had to go for a blood test at Addenbrooke's. It was lovely to go back. They made so much of William. He was treated like the hero returning – not only had he had a bone-marrow transplant, but he was part of a television programme. He looked well that day – in those first two or three days at home, he'd really picked up; you wouldn't believe the difference in him. After that, I don't believe for the next week he went to sleep at all during the day. He got up in the morning and was up till ten at night. He had a marvellous week. He was eating, obviously not much, but the difference in a few days was unbelievable; he was drinking; he was taking his medication, and he was generally just very happy. And he was looking forward to his birthday.'

William's progress did not last. Ten days after his return home, he began to feel sleepy. It was hard to keep him awake. He went off his food. On Sunday Sue rang the Royal Free Hospital.

'I said he wasn't too well. We hadn't got a thermometer – we'd left it in the sun on the window sill, and it had cooked and wouldn't come down. So we couldn't take his temperature. But we knew he was slightly feverish. The Royal Free said, "If you're really worried, bring him back now." But William was due to go to the hospital next day anyway. He had to have his Hickman catheter removed, and a lumbar puncture, and a bone-marrow test. So we waited till Monday. He was staying in overnight in any case, but I went prepared to stay longer. I took a bag with me.'

After the textbook success of William's treatment so far, his setback was a disappointment. It was as if they had all prepared themselves for a marathon, but had been excused the last few miles because the race had gone so well – only to be recalled to finish the course after all, when the muscles had relaxed and the adrenalin had ceased to flow. They tried not to give way. Sue was upset at this reverse, but although William could not have his Hickman catheter removed, she still hoped to bring him home for his birthday the following week.

Dr Roderick was again in charge of William day by day.

'We didn't know,' he says, 'why William had a fever. We could only look carefully to see if there was anything obviously infected. But there are probably whole hosts of things we don't even know exist . . . particularly viruses. We have very limited techniques of isolating these things. We couldn't find out what was causing the problem. It was worrying, because some viral infections can be quite severe – patients can die from them. But nothing worrying had developed. Medically, William was still pretty well. His blood counts were all right.'

Dr Brenner did, however, have an explanation for William's drowsiness.

'One of the major effects of radiation – William's total body irradiation – is on the brain. Various changes take place, which are very little understood – changes in the secretion of the hormones, changes in whatever the cells of the brain do. And about six weeks after radiotherapy, patients do get this somnolence.

'The infection, again, is very common. About half the patients after transplant get some kind of infection which is nothing to do with the graft, but simply due to the time taken for the new immune system to establish itself. The commonest sites are the sinuses, the lungs, the blood and the Hickman catheter – which is why we often remove the Hickman catheter before people leave hospital: on the other hand, if the patient does get sick after discharge. It's nice to have the Hickman to give all the antibiotics. So in William's case we left it in.

'We took samples from that, and from the kidneys and the stools and so on, but we found nothing. So we treated the infection blindly, with broad-spectrum antibiotics. Then we went on to antifungal drugs, because people who don't respond to antibiotics often have a little focus of fungus growing somewhere in their body.'

Initially, William was put on a five-day course of antibiotics. He seemed to have lost his zest, and the whole family found it difficult to readjust to hospital life – everything seemed to have changed. In one respect, life was easier: people going into William's room no longer had to wear gowns and masks. But in most others, Sue found it harder.

'We were in a different room. William's old room was needed for a post-transplant patient. We were three doors along – and everything was back to front. We didn't have a telephone, and to begin with, we couldn't get the television to work. We were in the same hospital, with the same people, but the student nurses had changed. They didn't know us or William; they didn't know how bright he'd been before. There was no school teacher. After a little while, Dr Roderick moved on. Sister Jordan went on holiday. Little Eduardo and his parents had gone to Portugal after his second block of chemotherapy. Helen wasn't there, either. William wanted to go and see her on the day he came back into hospital, before he got shut in his room, but Sister Jordan took me on one side and told me that she'd been transferred to the intensive therapy unit. I didn't tell William – I just said she wasn't there. But he found out. It was a shock. I thought I was going to see her so much better after the fortnight we'd been at home. She'd had a bad three weeks after her transplant, but then she rallied and Patra went home. A fortnight later she was in intensive care.'

Helen was facing a grave disadvantage in her fight for life. She carried within her a virus against which her sister's bone-marrow gave little protection. Dr Brenner was familiar with the situation. 'A major cause of death after transplant is a virus called cyto-megalovirus (CMV). It's a virus that's latent in sixty per cent of all adults in the United Kingdom, though the figure is much lower for children. In Greece and the Middle East, as many as ninety-five in a hundred carry it. It lives in the tissue quietly; but if the immune system is destroyed, it can creep out and disseminate itself through the bloodstream. If it gets into the lungs when they've been damaged by radiation, it causes pneumonitis, pneumonia, which is ninety per cent fatal.

'We find that if, when tested, you prove negative – that's to say, if you don't carry antibodies to the virus – your risk from this virus is extremely low. If you're positive, as Helen was, and your donor is positive, even then, oddly enough, your risk is low. The donor's immune system can actually protect you. Helen, though it wasn't known at the time, was in an extremely poor risk group – people who are positive themselves and who have donors who are negative. So they have the virus themselves, and then they have a new immune system that has no way of coping with that virus. In one group we studied recently, in that situation, forty-six per cent died of pneumonitis. The difficulty is that we can't vaccinate against the virus. We'd like to, but there isn't a vaccine. So Helen was in a very difficult situation.

'In William's case, the test was CMV negative – he hadn't got the virus. Very few British children have. Since there wasn't that particular risk, I didn't think I would burden Sue and Tim with that information, but just tell them the overall chances. It's difficult to know what to do – with so much to take in, parents can easily be overloaded. But if there had been a risk, I would have discussed it.'

Strangely, the information did percolate through to Sue in the end. Malcolm Brenner, while explaining the threat from cyto-megalovirus to me, told me that William's test was negative. I passed the good news on to Julia, who in turn passed it on to Sue before the transplant took place.

In the week after William's return to hospital, his course of antibiotics came to an end without any change in his condition. A second course of anti-fungal drugs was prescribed, together with a drug to minimize his sickness. Waiting anxiously for results, Sue decided to sleep in William's room. He was carefully monitored for side-effects, and he slept for much of the time. Sue was convinced that he was very ill. He had, she says, lost all his drive.

William's birthday came and went. Julia and the film crew came to film him, laying pale and asleep in his bed, barely aware of the decorations and the birthday cards strung all round the room.

The day afterwards, little Eduardo Cunha and his mother returned from Portugal for Eduardo's third block of chemotherapy. For Eduardo the outlook was still very much in doubt, but not hopeless.

A few days later, Helen's mother, Patra, returned from Greece. The doctors had found it difficult to communicate with her husband, Vasil. Tim was sharing a room with Vasil; and with Helen's survival now in the balance, he and Sue had been worried that Vasil might leave it too late for Patra to get back in time.

Tim took Vasil to Heathrow airport to meet Patra. Vasil was crying. 'He hadn't dared to tell Patra what the situation was. Then it all came out on the journey back – a Mediterranean explosion, a terrible row between the two of them, venting their frustration and disappointment on each other and on the hospital. I couldn't understand a word, but I knew what was being said: why didn't you tell me she was so ill? I'd have come sooner. I didn't want to tell you. What's the hospital done to her . . . and on and on and on. I had to switch off and just drive.

'At the hospital, it was some time before Vasil could take Patra to see Helen. Helen had plastic film over her eyes to stop them drying out. He desperately wanted it removed before Patra saw her. I'd got an English–Greek dictionary so that I could communicate with him, but it took me an hour to explain that it was a temporary thing, for Helen's good. I don't think he fully understood till much later. But in intensive care, absolutely everything was monitored. Patra couldn't believe it when she saw Helen.'

Sue never visited Helen in intensive care.

'I never saw her after we went home. When we came back into hospital, it took about a week before we realized that Helen wasn't going to make it. When Patra came back, she realized after about twenty-four hours that Helen was going to die. She used to walk round the corridor on the ward with me, and she'd wave and blow William a kiss. She and Vasil wanted to wish William well, but you thought: if only they didn't have to see William doing so well. Tim and I were worried, but in comparison with Helen, William was well. Then she wanted to go into the children's playroom – we were arm in arm – and there were Helen's dolls. She'd had three dolls on the window-sill of her room: Vasil must have left them behind when Helen was taken into intensive care. Patra went straight to one of the dolls and picked it up. Until Helen died, you would just see her cradling this doll, rocking and singing . . . squatting down, chanting to it. Then she'd stop. I'd make her a cup of coffee. We'd start a conversation, and there'd be laughing amidst all these tears. For a quarter of an hour it was lovely to see her laugh. But it was so short-lived. In a few minutes she would be back again – chanting and rocking.'

William's temperature was still above normal. He was still lethargic and being sick. To counter the sickness he had the anti-nausea drug given via the Hickman line; but a fortnight after his return, it was decided to try the drug in tablet form.

Sue was with him. 'The tablets started at mid-day. He took the first one, and carried on watching TV while we played cards. After an hour or so, he started to lick his lips. His tongue wouldn't stay in his mouth. I said, "William, don't do that." He just ignored me . . . he said, "I'm not doing anything." Then he started to look at me strangely – it seemed as if he had no control over his head, and his tongue was coming out all the more; it wouldn't fit in his mouth.

'I could feel the panic coming – this tablet wasn't suiting him. (It didn't matter what medicine he took, you always looked for a reaction.) I went out of the room, and said to the sister, "William's behaving a bit strangely." She came in, and immediately called the doctor, who came at once. William's head was right back, his tongue was out, his eyes were rolling backwards. The doctor just said straight away, "Oh this is a case of oculogyric crisis" – it was the word "crisis" that was so frightening. And the doctor admitted that this was the first time he'd seen it. He didn't say, "Don't worry . . . it'll be all right." He said, "I'll have to give him an injection – I don't know if we've got one on the ward. If not, I'll try and get one."

'So he went off to get it and I was left alone with William – there was a student nurse, but she didn't know anything about it. I was frightened, and William could see I was frightened. He asked me: "Am I going to intensive care?" And then he said, "I think I'm going to die."

'We must have been waiting for about ten minutes. Fortunately there was the right kind of injection on the ward. The doctor was soon back and gave it to William. By that time William was shouting out about the banging in his ears . . . he kept putting his hands to his ears and saying, "The noise . . . the banging!" He was really crying out with it. The injection was put in slowly and after twenty minutes the banging stopped. Within half an hour William was quiet again.'

Dr Roderick was not present when William had his fit, but he was familiar with the phenomenon. 'Most people have no trouble with this particular anti-sickness drug. But sometimes it affects the nerves that control eye movements. The eyes go up and down. The receptors of the nerves get blocked and you sometimes get uncontrolled neck movements: the neck twists and contorts. The whole control of the limbs, especially the head and neck, is disturbed. It's very frightening, but it's not life-threatening. It's easily reversed by simply giving the antidote.'

Sue knew how frightened William had been. 'That was the first time William thought he wasn't going to be all right. It wasn't far away, that fear, all the time after he went back to hospital, he was so low.'

The doctor insisted to Tim that William was not really ill. 'They said he simply had a temperature, an infection; but they couldn't identify it or locate it. And there was so much else going on, with

Helen being so ill; and the length of time we'd been involved with the whole thing . . . it was getting difficult to cope with at that stage. It was a bad time.' Nonetheless, next day Sue went home on one of her regular visits.

The following night Helen died.

Almost at once, Helen's parents moved out of the hospital into the home of the official Greek interpreter. Vasil expected Helen to be buried immediately, in accordance with Greek custom. He was baffled by the formalities of arranging for her body to be flown back to her own country. Tim did his best to explain the requirements of bureaucracy.

William was not told of Helen's death at first. When Sue came back to London, she noticed a difference in him: 'For three or four days he hadn't asked about Helen – and he always used to ask. I talked to David, the charge nurse, and told him William was very down. David said, "Perhaps he fears the worst, and doesn't like to ask." So I went in and sat down and told him, and that it was for the best – she would have suffered if she'd gone on. William cried. He said, "I thought I'd be able to say goodbye." He felt cheated.'

William was now at the end of his ten-day course of anti-fungal drugs. His temperature was still high. He did not seem to be responding. Dr Brenner came to the conclusion that the most likely remaining source of infection was the Hickman catheter. It was time to get rid of it.

'What often happens is that at the bottom of the catheter a little blood-clot forms, and that can be infected. But you never culture the infection, the bug, because the antibiotics suppress it, though they can't actually get into the blood-clot to kill it. But we always leave removal of the Hickman to last, unless there is evidence to implicate it as the cause, because we need it for antibiotics while we're treating the other possibilities.'

William was taken to the operating theatre and given a general anaesthetic. Removing the Hickman catheter was not difficult. It could simply be pulled out. The hole, where the catheter had entered the vein leading to William's heart, closed up and sealed itself.

Sue treated the operation as routine. It still represented progress, to have the Hickman removed. After all, that was what they had come into hospital for three weeks earlier. But if the site of infection had been cleared, William's temperature should have returned to normal within twenty-four hours. It failed to match the doctors' expectations.

In the room next door, little Eduardo's temperature was considerably higher than William's. Contact between the two boys was difficult, but they could signal their presence by bouncing balls against the dividing wall. Eduardo was finding his third block of chemotherapy, though not as bad as the first, still hard going. His mother was worried by his persistent fever. She telephoned her husband in Portugal, and asked him to rejoin her.

It was only when Edwards reached London that he realized that a bone-marrow transplant for little Eduardo was a real possibility. 'The word "transplant" was mentioned since the first or second day in Portugal – but I didn't know what it was, a transplant. I couldn't imagine. They only explained it to me on the third course of chemotherapy. They said that with the bone-marrow transplant, if we get a real match of a donor, the chances for Eduardo are coming up. So they said that when we finished the third course of chemotherapy, they would allow us to go four weeks to Portugal, to see if we can get a match. If we get one, we have to decide if we want a bone-marrow transplant, or not. If not, they have to try the fourth course of chemotherapy. That's the way they were explaining it. But without the transplant, they didn't know about the chances. With the fourth course of chemotherapy they didn't know what would happen.'

Two days after William's Hickman catdeter was removed, his temperature began to come down, but remained stubbornly just above normal.

Sue watched the chart hour by hour: 'He still had a temperature – but he was better in himself. He was allowed to leave his room. He even sat outside on Sunday afternoon on the hospital wall. Then he had to have a blood transfusion. The red cells, the haemoglobin, were a bit low, and had to be topped up before he could go home. Of course, he had to have the transfusion via a drip in his arm, now the Hickman had gone. Suddenly he became panicky: 'How can I go to sleep having a blood transfusion?' – whereas at Addenbrooke's he'd been so good at having a drip in his hand, he never worried. But this time he became so tense that I slept in his room again. It finished at three in the morning, and the staff nurse took it out.

'Whenever you have a blood transfusion, your temperature goes up. So we thought: That's another twenty-four hours before we can go home. But William's didn't. It went down, and never went up any more. Four days after the Hickman was taken out we were home again. After three weeks! Those three weeks seemed a lifetime.'

CHAPTER 22

Before William's infection, Sue and Tim had planned to take all the children on holiday for the first fortnight in August. When William was finally fit enough to leave the Royal Free Hospital for the second time, Sue and Tim decided to take advantage of the last remaining days of their booking. William was still very weak. On the day of his discharge, his Uncle Duffy had had to carry him on his back when they went for a stroll outside the hospital. William felt queasy on the journey to Norfolk and, as soon as he got out of the car, was sick on the garden path. But Sue still felt it was better not to stay at home.

'We decided to go on holiday because psychologically it would do William far more good than to convalesce at home. We felt he needed the satisfaction of going on holiday. We asked the hospital, and they didn't object. So next day, the Wednesday morning, we loaded up, went and fetched the others from Grandma's and away we went. We took the trailer and just put everything in, bicycles, the lot. It was funny, but this time it wasn't a chore. We just thought: great! Let's go and enjoy ourselves.

'We went to a village on the north Norfolk coast, Heacham, with a promenade, a sea-wall really, that runs all the way to Hunstanton, about a mile. It's where the silt gets washed out from the Ouse, so the beach is very muddy and sticky – lots of cockles and mussels, and the tide goes out for at least a mile. William had been there the year before. We hired a caravan.'

To William it was a holiday to be remembered. 'There was a great big row of caravans and beach-huts and chalets. We hired Harriet's godmother's caravan. You just went over the wall and there was the beach. I couldn't swim because of the hole where the Hickman had been, but I went in the paddling boat – I paddled out, but my rope was tied to a bit of wood on the beach. It was good fun, having all the family together again.'

Sue had no problem keeping William away from other people. The caravan stood on its own plot, with the beach adjoining it. William had his own room in the caravan, where Sue would look after him..

'He was still on mouthwashes and tablets and strict clean-care.

We had to set up a hospital routine in his own room. All the cooking had to be done so that it didn't need microwaving – we hadn't brought the microwave. He couldn't have fish and chips when we did. He had to have properly cooked food, served immediately – and served to him first.

'But he had a marvellous holiday. Within twenty-four, thirty-six hours, he was a different child again. He was hairless, and very thin and wobbly. But during the day he didn't sleep at all. That was the amazing thing: whereas he'd been sleeping a lot and it had been a job to wake him up, he was awake all day, and keeping up with the others. It was fine – no problem at all. We were all so pleased to be together. The only mishap was when Harriet rode her bicycle over William's radio-controlled car and broke the front axle.

'But although things had gone so well and we'd come so far, Tim and I realized how quickly he could get an infection and be back in hospital. We knew we weren't out of the wood yet. We cherished every day, and that holiday was a holiday that we were going to make sure we enjoyed and were always going to remember. We enjoyed it so much that we decided to book the caravan for the children's half-term in October.

'Even when we got back home, life was still like a holiday. The children would give me treats. I couldn't imagine ever being cross with William again. But I suppose after two or three weeks, life had to get back to some kind of normality. Once school started again for the three younger children, I said, "Well, let's put this all behind us"; but even school didn't seem normal – taking them to school again was something new. The thing I found hard was the household chores – to get back into the routine of housework.

'I think I felt physically tired, mentally tired, exhausted. All the strength God had given me seemed suddenly to go, but you had to find new strength to carry on with day-to-day life. And people were inclined to leave me on my own because of isolation restrictions. I partly wanted that, but I felt that some of them also tended to think that all our troubles were over. They assumed that William was cured. He was out of hospital. He had a home tutor coming in. The other children were at school.'

September brought William's three months' check-up at the Royal Free Hospital. The results were good, but like Sue, Tim found that people outside the family did not understand their purely provisional nature. 'They saw William looking all right. They assumed he must be cured. "William's well now, is he?" they'd say. It was irritating, because we didn't want to think about it; but we kept our feelings to ourselves. We'd say, "Yes, he's fine." And he was fine, as far as it went. You don't bother people with your worries, do you?'

But Sue knew that William was not really well. Every day she had to persuade him to eat, drink, take his tablets and his mouthwash. In hospital she had had the support of the doctors and nurses; now, she was on her own – and she had the other children to look after. 'When they went back to school and I was trying to get back to normal, they couldn't have everything they wanted any more; and they would react. They would say, "It wasn't like this when you were away. We were allowed to do this or that. We could choose what food we wanted." The three of them played up – possibly Harriet more than the others, because she'd had a lot of attention while we were away.' For a time Sue had to be quite firm with the younger children, William simply seemed pleased to be at home.

Meanwhile, the BBC had not yet finished their programme. About three weeks after William left hospital, Julia and the crew came to see how he was getting on and to film him. William wasn't allowed any visitors at home, except relatives, so they took him out bicycling with two of his friends. Harriet was jealous.

Later that autumn Sue's problems took a different form. 'When I had more or less got the three younger ones sorted out, I couldn't believe it when William started. Having been so good all this time, he became edgy. I suppose I was on at him all day to do this, do that. I can remember him pointing at me and saying, "You're always nagging me. Leave me alone." And when you think about it, I used to say to William: "What would you like to eat?" "I'm not hungry." "William, you must eat something" – and I'd get something, and he'd just pick at it. I suppose for three months I was harassing him to eat, even if it was only a mouthful. I had to, or he would just never have eaten a thing. If he didn't eat his scrambled egg, half an hour later I'd be offering him an apple – which had to be peeled first with a sterile knife and put on a sterile plate. And he might eat half of it. Because he had to eat little and often, the whole day I was asking him, "What do you fancy? An apple? A banana? A packet of crisps?" Just anything.

'He began to make a fuss about doing the routine things. It used to take an hour, four times a day, to make him take his tablets and his mouthwashes and lozenges (well, *you* try and take something antiseptic in your mouth and swill it round when you're off your food and feeling queasy; and then suck a lozenge under your tongue till it breaks up). The lozenges weren't that nasty, but they weren't things you wanted to have to take four times a day. They were chalky. You could see it round his mouth.

'The mouthwash would take quarter of an hour, twenty minutes. And he would put it off. He'd say, "Right, I'm going to do it now", and then go off to the toilet. We'd go through this routine – "I'm going to do it now" – and the phone would ring, someone perhaps I hadn't spoken to for six weeks, bombarding me with questions about William and his illness . . . what did it mean . . . what was going to happen . . . was he cured? The same old thing over and over again whenever anybody rang. I got sick of telling people. They'd ask questions I didn't know the answers to and didn't want to know the answers to. But I felt obliged to talk to them. I couldn't be rude. It sounds ungrateful, but if I was feeling low it was difficult to cope with. And I'd been on the phone half an hour, and William still hadn't finished his mouthwash. I'd be cross with the person I'd been speaking to, and then I'd give it to William for not getting on. He'd be cross that I hadn't been with him – it was a vicious circle. And then the phone would ring again, and you could still see the mouthwash sitting there.

'I suppose he was tired of being nagged, and I was tired of nagging. I felt we'd been through so much in hospital – why couldn't he just get on and do it at home? Why did we keep going through this battle every day? I got so cross that I felt: Oh, I hate you. And I expected him to say, "And I hate you, too." Perhaps it would have been better if we'd just stood there and said that.

'He realized he was being annoying and frustrating. He would apologize afterwards. But you just had to build up to that pitch. He would turn round and say, "I can't stop myself. I can't just get on with it."

'But then he had his own feelings to sort out as well. About that time, he cried every night for a week when he went to bed. He would say, "I'm remembering Helen." He didn't think it was fair that she should have died, while he lived.

'We were very isolated, the two of us shut up together. I didn't have friends around for coffee or anything like that, because the risk of infection was too great. In hospital there'd always been people to talk to, and visitors as well; and there were cards and letters. All that stopped when William came home, all the special treatment and the contacts; we were left to get on with it.'

Tim was not subject to quite the same pressures. He was able to get out of the house and go to work. On the other hand, the business badly needed his attention: 'It was a question of getting ready for Christmas. That's the big time of year for us. And we had to get on with the backlog of jewellery work that my assistant, David, hadn't been able to do. The ironic thing is that from September on we hit the worst period of that year. From the moment I got back into harness again, the turnover began to dip. Two jewellers in the High Street had closed during the year, with half-price sales. So if anybody was going to spend any money on jewellery, they would have spent it at those sales. Consequently, the Christmas jewellery budget, which I might have got a slice of, didn't come to me. But luckily the antiques were making up for it.'

William's illness had brought Sue and Tim closer together. Their united purpose, their shared faith and their mutual support during the struggle to bring William through had strengthened the bond between them. But in one sense William's long ordeal had diverted their attention away from each other.

For Sue the process had begun some time before. 'To start with, in hospital we never shared the same bed for long at a time. That didn't matter. But obviously there were times when we did have our own bedroom. Around transplant time and afterwards, I became quite claustrophobic when Tim put his arms around me and cuddled up. I felt myself fighting it – I couldn't relax in that way. Tim could. I think that's a man – the difference between male and female. We didn't have arguments. Tim could understand it. But it was a difficulty that we had to get over when we got home. And it was still a slight problem, depending on how William was . . . because to me, if William was a bit off colour, that was the first thing I could do without, thank you.

'On the other hand, I don't think Tim realized how lonely I was after William came home. He didn't see that I was running into trouble. But at the beginning of October when William went back to London for his monthly check-up and an eye test, the hospital talked to us and asked how everything was at home. And they offered us an appointment with the child psychologist.'

But Sue was not entirely the victim of loneliness and depression. 'In October, when I made the beds, I would get out the computer game Rosemary's son, Alexei, had given William, and listen to the tune it played. And I did the same with the keyboard the swimming club gave him. That was programmed to play "Twinkle, Twinkle, Little Star". Something made me want to listen to them. I couldn't understand how

I felt . . . it was a mixture of sadness and happiness. They took me back to the early days when William was so ill.

'I remember talking about it one day to Rosemary. Rosemary said, "It was the love of it all – they brought back all the love." And all of a sudden, when Rosemary had left, something dawned on me. It was as though – how can I describe it – as though suddenly I'd seen God, as though I'd had a vision. I felt so happy that day, because all at once everything was explained to me: it was the love in everything that had got me through, the love in absolutely everything. There was no one who'd been nasty, unkind, who'd said a cross word.'

The occasion made an impression on Rosemary, too. 'I can remember Sue phoning me up to say thank you – I stood there with tears streaming down my face, which sounds silly now.'

'But I'd learnt something very important that day,' Sue adds. 'Those sounds will be in my mind for ever. It's as though I was hunting to find out why. And Rosemary was saying to me: "It was just love".'

To Rosemary it was so obvious. 'I couldn't see why she couldn't see it. And yet it's a word we're all frightened of – frightened of admitting we need it and we want it and we like it.'

CHAPTER 23

At the beginning of September, little Eduardo Cunha and his parents left London for their home in Oporto. Eduardo, after three blocks of chemotherapy, was in remission. If a donor could be found, he was a suitable candidate for a bone-marrow transplant. In Portugal his father arranged for tissue tests for himself, his wife, and his daughter, Joanna. 'We made the tests on Monday. We were supposed to come back to London on Friday or Saturday. They said, "OK, this is an exception. We will give you the results on Wednesday." I went on Wednesday, and they did not have the results. I went on Thursday again – and they still did not have the results. But suddenly a doctor came, and she was smiling. And she said, "I'm not allowed to tell you, but it seems they match. Eduardo and Joanna match." And I talked with a senior doctor, and she said, "With this kind of match, go ahead and have the transplant."

'The transplant was already arranged in London. We came to London and they did the tests on Joanna. But there was something wrong in the cells of my daughter. So they repeated the test; and they said, "Don't worry – it's only a few cells, two or three per cent."

'With the transplant, I only think: why can't we have the same facilities in Portugal? The Hickman, for example, is a wonderful thing. And the laboratory – they can give you the results of a blood count in two or three minutes. That is wonderful technology. But the TBI, the total body irradiation – I saw it; and there are some things it's better not to see. Because I think it is one of the worst things they do with the patients. I can't imagine how to stay in one position for one hour . . . I can't stay more than five or ten minutes. And then Eduardo started crying that he couldn't move, and that his bottom had pain. "I want to pass urine." He was so bad. And that kind of noise . . . Zzzz . . .

'In one sense it's better not to know what's happening. But as we had stayed with our son all the time, from the first day, we wanted to know everything and stay with him. I used to say, "When a strong man is alone, he can be a coward. When two cowards are together, they can be strong." That happened with us – if I was crying or upset, my wife told me: "It's not the time for that. We have to be together fighting." When she was at that stage, it's me who tells her, "You can't do that now. If you want to cry, go away, cry, and finish it. Then come back."

'We had some stages when we refused to eat . . . that was probably stupid, because we have to survive – if we don't survive, we can't help him. But if Eduardo had a problem, sometimes we were in the ward, looking at the watch and saying, "We still have half an hour of the treatment – oh God, make this treatment finish, so we can go to the canteen." And then we didn't want to go there.

'And we stopped sleeping together. We had separate lives. One night I would sleep with my son, one night it was my wife – that is, when we were allowed, because at the beginning we were not allowed, and we used to stay outside in the small hall with two chairs. For example, I stayed till three, four o'clock in the morning; and then my wife came and stayed in the hall outside, and I slept. It is wonderful to me – during the time we stayed in the hospital, four or five hours' sleep was enough.'

On 27 October, Eduardo received a transplant of his sister Joanna's bone-marrow.

In Norfolk, William was making good progress. He was still unable to have visitors at home, but he used to go with the three younger children to the village school and shout to his friends over the fence. He was fitter and could walk round the outside of the playing-field, kicking a football back when it went out of play.

The day after Eduardo's transplant was the beginning of half-term in Terrington St John. Sue and Tim and the four children went back to the caravan at Heacham. The holiday didn't turn out as Sue expected.

'Poor old William was ill from the morning we got up to go. He'd been fine since the holiday in August until October. He'd had no medical problems at all. He'd been perfectly well and healthy, slowly building up all the time. And that morning he was sick. We went from Tuesday to Saturday, and he was ill the whole time. We were up with him at night; he had tummy pains, a temperature, diarrhoea. And I was in a state again. I spent my nights crying – next week we were going to be back in hospital. But he wasn't so bad that I felt I ought to ring the hospital; and by the last day of the holiday, he wasn't sick, although he still had diarrhoea. The infection went away as quickly as it came, but it was unfortunate. We thought we were taking William away for a break, and every day he was ill. And it was supposed to be a break for me, too – to get away from being shut up in the house – but it wasn't.'

A few days later, Sue and Tim took William to London for his monthly check-up. All was well. Sue and Tim took the opportunity to talk to one of the hospital's child psychologists about their difficulties in adjusting to normal life.

'Basically,' says Sue, 'what emerged was that I needed a break. Tim could get away and go to work, think of other things; but I was with William all day, every day. I suppose, that day, I got rid of some tension. Tim, perhaps, understood a bit better how I felt. He took a day off work a few days later and looked after William. I went out for the day – I went shopping with my Mum. And later the doctor wrote a report, reassuring us that we didn't have any real problem – nothing we couldn't deal with. It was just the normal difficulty of getting back to family life. We didn't really feel we had a problem. It was just something we took the chance to discuss before we did have a problem. And from then on things improved.'

On 2 December the Royal Free Hospital announced that William had progressed well enough for all treatment to cease. Henceforward he could begin to live a normal life. He was able to mix with people indoors. He could go to the school's Christmas party. Forbidden foods, like fresh milk, cream, ice-cream, yoghurt and salads, could be gradually introduced into his meals. However, the last effects of the treatment, particularly the radiation, on his lungs and intestines were not expected to disappear for another six months – a year after the transplant.

On 8 January William went back to school. That evening, on BBC2, the BBC transmitted the '40 Minutes' film about William's experiences, also called 'Just for William'. To mark the occasion, both the BBC and Anglia Television sent film crews to film William in school and interview him for that evening's regional current affairs programmes. It was not the kind of day Sue had imagined for William's return. I could only join in the celebrations by telephone, being occupied in making current affairs films in Northern Ireland.

Sue and Tim had already seen 'Just for William' in November at a preview in London arranged by Julia; to my relief, and Julia's, they approved of it. William and the other children saw a videotape of the film a day later. In the next few weeks they watched it four or five times. Harriet said that it was only the film that had persuaded her that she had really given William her bone-marrow – after her terror in hospital at the preparations for the bone-marrow harvest, she had wiped the memory from her mind, and denied that she had ever been the donor. Naomi commented, correctly, that the film wasn't really meant for children, and added that William liked grown-up programmes anyway. William, characteristically, took the showing of the film in his stride, and displayed few signs of big-headedness even when it became clear that it had made him famous overnight. Next day he took a day off school to appear with Sue and Tim on one of the BBC's daytime programmes, 'Open Air', and was later invited to take part in 'Top of the Pops'. Letters poured in, to him, to Harriet, and to Sue and Tim, more than two hundred and fifty in all. William became a local celebrity and was asked to take part in one charity event after another. Sue had to limit his appearances.

In London, life was harder for little Eduardo and his family. Big Eduardo was still in England.

'After the transplant everything was, let's say, in a normal way . . . not very good, not bad. The only thing which was not normal were the platelets. They were lazy platelets, they were not coming up. But one day the doctor said, "If everything is going on like this, in one week, two weeks' time, you can go home . . . when the platelets come up." But they did not come up.

'Then Eduardo started a bit of a rash. And after a few days they said, "Probably it's 'graft versus host' disease." "Oh, what's that?" I asked. And they explained to me: at the beginning they didn't explain. They said they needed a liver biopsy, a stomach test. And everything showed GVH.

'But OK – I knew the Royal Free was one of the best, because they had discovered something about GVH. So they gave Eduardo steroids, a small dose. And they said that in two weeks he would be fine. And in two weeks he was miserable. The doctor said, "Oh, sometimes steroids make them feel happy, sometimes they make them feel miserable. But he is not better: we have to increase steroids. In four, five days he will be better." In four, five days my son was worse. And he was gradually coming down with a lot of symptoms. His stomach didn't work, his intestines didn't work, so we couldn't give drink, couldn't do anything.

'But a worse time came . . . when the doctors told me there was nothing else they could do for my son. Everything they knew, they had done for my son; and it was not working. And all the time they looked at my son and they said, "He's really unlucky, this boy. Everything

happened to him – and he was supposed to have nothing like this."
For a few moments, or a few hours, I despaired. "Oh God," I said,
"it's not fair, because we suffer too much."

'For about four weeks we had a good graft. So why did it go wrong?
As I said before, I trust the doctors. But with this happening, I tried to
find something wrong with them. I wanted an excuse, a reason to
blame them. This terrible thing must not happen – the chances for it
to happen with my son are too low . . . just two or three per cent of the
cells in the graft. And I found an excuse. I found that, for example,
when the rash started, I told the doctors; and they only did something
one week later. I said, "Oh God, if only they started with the procedure
when I told them. I told them, but they forgot." In a certain way I can
blame them, but in another way I can't. As they explained to me, they
were expecting the GVH in the palms of the hands and the soles of the
feet – and he had nothing there. His rash came on the right side of the
neck, the left side of the neck, and then came down. It's not fair to
blame the doctors.

'Then one of the doctors talked with me, and he said, "The only
thing we can do is try something new. We never tried it before with
leukaemia patients. We have used it – not in this hospital but in
another hospital – with other kinds of cancer. It's not in the experimental stage, it is a bit beyond that, and if you agree we will use it with
your son." Well, if there is nothing else, what to do? I decided on the
spot, and then I told my wife. Usually in my family we decide together,
me, my wife and my mother-in-law. But this was not to be decided like
that.

'The results of the new drug, the experiment, were something like
this. The first day the new medicine was working about forty per cent;
the second day seventy per cent; the third day ninety per cent; and the
fourth day it was the last dose to consolidate. And they said, "Finally,
it works." And it worked. It worked in the end.'

Malcolm Brenner was extremely worried about Eduardo's prospects
when GVH was diagnosed: 'GVH is fatal in a considerable proportion
of cases, and in a very horrible way. Eduardo was lucky to get through
it. But in a way he was lucky that he had it: a graft that attacks the host
has a strong anti-leukaemic effect as well. It attacks the leukaemic
cells. But frankly, we'd rather avoid it. The benefits are considerably
less than the ill-effects.'

Little Eduardo's troubles were not over. He fell prey to infections.
Christmas came and went. He and his parents were touched by the

visits and cards from doctors and nurses they had encountered. But the strain of the long-drawn-out campaign began to tell. They began to have misunderstandings over insignificant issues – the availability of sleeping accommodation, the use of the school's tape recorders, the level of teaching. Understanding the nuances of English was still difficult, and, mistakenly or not, from time to time they began to feel they were being discriminated against because they were not British.

Little Eduardo lost a lot of weight. When he began to put it back on, the steroids he was prescribed gave his face a puffy appearance. But gradually his condition improved. In February, eleven months after his diagnosis, he was allowed out of hospital. The family moved into a flat nearby so that he could be kept under surveillance.

Then, one day when Eduardo and his father were out shopping, his father spoke to him – and got no reply. He spoke to him again, more sharply. Again no reply. Eventually he discovered that little Eduardo could hardly hear in one ear. One of the antibiotics needed to deal with his last infection had damaged his hearing.

Little Eduardo summed up the family's reaction: better deaf than dead.

CHAPTER 24

February brought William another reminder that he must not take too much for granted. For a week he felt too ill to go to school. At the weekend he looked pale and tired. To casual visitors like myself, the whiteness of his lips was alarming.

Sue took William to their own doctor, Ken Doran.

'It is very frightening,' he says, 'when you see a child like that . . . you feel, is he ever going to respond? But provided the signs were reasonable – provided the haemoglobin was higher than the skin colour might have suggested, and provided his white count and platelets were OK – then I wasn't too worried. The only hiccup was when he had a throat infection. That knocked him back for about three weeks . . . he wasn't doing well, and Sue asked me to look at him several times.

'On this occasion, I expected to find an infection, but it wasn't there. I avoided giving antibiotics, because if they didn't work I would have ruined any tests the Royal Free did. But when William went to London for his nine-month check-up, they did put him on antibiotics. They also managed to grow something, grow a bug – but since it's in ninety per cent of the population all the time, was it this that was causing the problem?'

'Within twenty-four hours,' says Sue, 'you could see the difference the antibiotics had made. But they never found any real infection.'

At the beginning of June, William visited London for his last formal examination. Henceforward he would be monitored locally. For the Royal Free Hospital, William's transplant was over. In the same month, Eduardo Cunha and his parents were allowed to go back to Portugal.

As far as anyone could tell, William was cured.

William sums up the position as he sees it. 'It's been a success. But we shan't know if I'm cured for about five years. So we shan't know if it was worth it for about five years. I feel OK. I feel back to normal; so I might as well forget it. I don't think about it much – at odd times, I think back to what I was doing a year ago. But it's much quicker, really, to have a transplant than to have to go through extra chemotherapy and radiation and wait for the count to pick up. I've gained something . . . I've gained time, really.'

In strictly scientific terms, there is no 'cure' for leukaemia. With every month that passes without a life-threatening infection or a recurrence of the malignancy, William's chances of surviving for a normal life-span improve. Having survived a year after his transplant, he would be very unlucky to fall victim again. In time, his case will be classified in the statistics under the heading: 'Survival for five years or more in remission'. That is as far as the doctors will go in claiming a cure: there can never be absolute certainty that the cancer will never return. On the other hand, if, after many years, a patient is struck down by a particular leukaemia for a second time, who is to say whether it is a recurrence of the old leukaemia or a new attack?

The price of William's illness was high. There is one instalment still to be paid, of which William has only recently become aware. Originally, Malcolm Brenner explained it to his parents: 'The effect of radiation on hormone function is that William will never produce fertile sperm. I don't think there is a reported case of a male having a bone-marrow transplant and producing viable sperm. The cells within the testes which produce sperm get damaged, and are never able to regenerate properly. So William will never be able to have children of his own. But his sexual development will be completely normal, because the hormones which produce sexual development and activity at puberty are much more sturdy and recover.'

The questions raised by this consequence of bone-marrow transplantation are for William to answer for himself in the future. For him, as for Eduardo, a particular handicap may have little weight in the scales of life and death. At the moment, it seems unfair to ask him either to look ahead too far or to analyse too deeply what he has already been through. Relying on the love and reassurance offered by his family, he fought for his life. He did everything he was asked. He displayed fortitude and maturity beyond his age.

William's response to the challenge of death was clearly influenced by the Christian faith expressed and taught by his parents. Since his recovery, he has followed the path of a conventional, but these days less than common, Christian upbringing. He has joined the village choir; he has given an organ recital for charity in the church; he has been confirmed by the bishop – before the secular influences of secondary education can act as a disincentive. So how does he now make sense of his experience of leukaemia?

'It's unfair,' William says, 'to anyone who has it, one out of three thousand, but someone's got to have it – that's what Mum said – and it was me. She said God knew from the moment I was born that when I was nine I would have leukaemia. I was a bit put off by that; but I didn't have time to be angry with God, with everything going on round me. Now I look back, I can see that God did help me through. I didn't actually realize it at the time. Mum and I used to pray together before I went to sleep, but I didn't really talk to God privately when I was lying in bed – I was too shattered, and it was ten o'clock at night and I had my tablets to think about: they took some getting down. It's only now, when I look back, that I see what God did. The programme helped, too, when I saw myself and what had happened – I couldn't remember a lot of it. That showed me how I was helped through.

'I got confirmed because Mum and Dad asked me if I wanted to. I thought about it for a few days and then I said "Yes". I've been a Christian all my life. Being a Christian means a lot to me. I feel God is always there when I need Him. When I'm really low, or if I relapse, God is going to help me through, like He did last time. I lost a year out of my life, but what I really gained was Christian faith. After my confirmation, that was when I could really see why it had all happened.'

About a year after William's transplant, a dozen members of his family met and discussed the events of the previous twelve months – and even further back. Sue expressed a paradoxical view.

'Obviously, I wish that William hadn't been ill; but it's done us all a lot of good. My faith is stronger. I pray far more than I did before. I can stand at the sink, washing-up, and talk to God. I do it most of the time – well, when the children aren't demanding something.

'Life will never be the same again . . . never, ever. It's returned to normal – as normal as we'll ever have – but I shan't take anything for granted any more . . . I shan't think that it will be there tomorrow.

'These last few months we have suffered, but they've made us appreciate everyone and everything. I shall never forget the help we got – even from people who may not speak to me much now. They were there when I needed them. And another thing – I learnt there were always people worse off than us. I think that would be true even if William had died.'

Tim's mother, Dorothy, looked back to the moment when the news came of William's diagnosis. 'I don't think we asked, "Why William?" You know the very first thing we did? We went before the Lord – and we got our friends to pray. There was a lot of prayer, up and down the

185

land, for William. And we know the Lord hears; and He answers – but not always in the way we expect, or in the way Tim hoped He would.'

'The lady who lives in the flat above the shop,' said Tim, 'she said to me one day, "With all the evil people there are in the world to have leukaemia, why does it have to be William?" That's a lot of people's reaction.'

To Tim's elder brother, Michael, that was not a tenable point of view.

'You know the Lord doesn't allow anything to happen without a purpose – at least I don't think so – but I don't think the question "Why?" matters the least little bit. You don't have to know the answer. All things work together for good to them that love God.

'There was an old man who came to our church in Cambridge, and one evening he described a tapestry: if you look at the back of it, he said, it's long strings and short strings and knots and cross-overs, and it doesn't make any sense at all. You look at the other side, the front, and, if it's done by a clever hand, it's beautiful. And he drew the analogy with life: we see the knots and the cross-overs and the short ends, and it doesn't make any sense. What God sees is the other side. That does help you to accept events like William's illness.'

An unbeliever might argue that for God to inflict suffering is cruel; and that nothing God does in the future, or in the next world, can undo the pain we endure now. Tim replied: 'That pain is cruel. But when Helen died, and Vasil was distraught with grief, I pointed out the comparison between God and a gardener who grows a wonderful rosebush. If he wants to pick one of the buds, he's entitled to do so. He doesn't have to let it flower on the tree. He can take that bud home early. That meant something to Vasil. But the irony was that, at the time William had his setback after the transplant and had to go back into hospital, when Helen was so ill and died, I felt – call it coincidence, if you will, or all things working together for good – I felt that William was ill at that period so that we would be in London when Vasil needed us. The doctors couldn't put their finger on anything to make William ill. He only went in for a check-up. He was only supposed to be in for a day. And yet we were there for three weeks.'

Eduardo Cunha has also come to terms with his son's illness, and can see good emerging from evil.

'In the beginning we were so angry. Why Eduardo? But that is not fair to other parents, it is not kind to ask, "Why *my* son?" So then we changed to "Why children?" But with Eduardo, I sometimes think:

Did I do something wrong? But, my God! there's lots of people doing wrong things, and nothing happens to them. And the question came again: "Why us? Why my son? Did I love him too much?"

'But then this happening to my son was an example to other people. I have a friend, about fifty years old. He had a daughter who was not married, but she had a son. My friend did not like the child – he did not like his daughter. I told him: "You can't blame your grandson, a little boy, two years old – he doesn't know what he's doing here with his feet on this earth. Probably you can't blame your daughter. Certainly, you can't blame yourself just because the education you gave your daughter was perhaps not the best – sometimes these things happen even with good education." But he could not look at his daughter or his grandson.

'But when I came back to Portugal the first time, he came to talk to me. He said, "I have come to love my grandson. What happened to Eduardo showed me how to look at children. I asked myself: What if it happened to my grandson? So now my grandson is going to the café with me, he goes everywhere with me. And I am glad I saw what happened to Eduardo."'

The Clayton family are all inclined to see the hand of divine providence, not only in William's illness but in the apparent accidents of daily life – Ann's presence on a six-week sister's course at Addenbrooke's in the first few days after William's diagnosis, David's proximity to both Cambridge and London, the division of labour between the two sides of the family. Most of all, Tim sees significance in his father's painfully prolonged death a year before.

'I don't think Pa was being made to suffer for anything he had done. I think he was suffering so that we could learn to cope with that . . . to pull us together very tightly as a family, so that when we came to see William suffering, we could deal with that more easily.'

But such thoughts do not preoccupy even William's immediate family for much of the time. For Sue, one image marks the moment when William put sickness and convalescence finally behind him.

'In the spring, William went away for a week's holiday with the school – it was a study expedition by the sea. Other mothers just took it for granted, but I felt: how lucky he was to go . . . and the thought did creep into my mind, what would the day have been like if he hadn't been here to go? I was so pleased – and at last he didn't have a load of tablets to take with him. He was normal.

'Some of the mothers said to me, "How do you dare send him

away?" Yet in a way they were more anxious than I was – getting on to the bus for a final kiss and checking all the luggage, and waving as the bus drove away.

'William didn't even look back.'

POSTSCRIPT

In the three years that have passed since William's transplant a number of changes to the procedure have begun to be introduced which are helping to make the process of marrow transplantation not only safer but also more widely applicable.

One of the major problems remaining in bone-marrow transplantation is the toxicity of the pre-transplant conditioning required to eliminate the patient's own bone-marrow and immune system. At present – and as given to William – this usually consists of high doses of toxic drugs and of whole body irradiation. Although this is an effective way of eliminating the patient's marrow, it is non-selective, damaging gut and lungs, and may cause death. Recently, monoclonal antibodies (MAb) which are able to recognize portions of the patient's immune system and destroy them in a highly selective fashion have begun to be used. These MAb are modified from antibodies of the kind used to treat William's marrow and prevent 'graft versus host' disease.

The second major problem associated with marrow transplantation has been the immune deficiency that follows the procedure due to the time taken for the immune system of the donor to redevelop in the patient. For up to a year, this leaves the recipient with an immune system that resembles the immune system of an individual with AIDS, so that transplant recipients are vulnerable to the same range of lethal infections as AIDS patients. Over the past few years, growth hormones for the human immune system have been made synthetically and are now under trial at the Royal Free Hospital and at other centres in Europe and America. Although it will take some time before we understand the best way of using these hormones, there is already evidence that they are able to be of benefit to the patients.

Finally, the applicability of bone-marrow transplantation is being broadened by our ability to find donors who are genetically matched, even though they are not from within the same family. It is now possible to analyse the tissue type of literally hundreds of thousands of volunteer donors until one is found who is a close genetic match to the patient. The ability to transplant successfully from these 'matched unrelated donors' will probably become increasingly important as families become smaller and the chances of finding a genetically matched member within the family correspondingly diminish.

In medicine there is usually a delay of years or even decades between a basic scientific discovery and its clinical application. Bone-marrow transplantation has been something of an exception, and the recent advances in biotechnology and genetic engineering have already begun to make their impact. The day when bone-marrow transplantation is considered a routine and relatively minor procedure may be rather closer than we think!

The Royal Free Hospital,   Dr M. K. Brenner
London
August 1988